Taste of Lifeline

Overeaters Anonymous, Inc.
World Service Office
PO Box 44020, Rio Rancho NM 87174-4020 USA
505-891-2664
www.oa.org

OA Board-Approved

Library of Congress Control Number: 2015905632
ISBN: 978-1-889681-11-5

PREFACE

The stories that fill these pages first appeared in *Lifeline,* the monthly magazine of Overeaters Anonymous. Published between 2005 and 2015, the stories are the work of OA members who write, not as professional authors, but as compulsive eaters who are recovering through the practice of OA's Twelve Step program.

Like all the stories and articles in *Lifeline,* these pieces reflect individual members' experiences and viewpoints, not necessarily those of OA as a whole.

We hope the reader enjoys this sampling from *Lifeline,* a rich resource documenting members' recovery.

CONTENTS

CONTENTS

CHAPTER FOUR: STEPS TEN TO TWELVE

CHAPTER FIVE: TOOLS OF RECOVERY

CONTENTS

CHAPTER SIX:
CARRYING THE MESSAGE THROUGH THE TOOLS OF SERVICE AND SPONSORSHIP

CHAPTER SEVEN: TRADITIONS

CONTENTS

CONTENTS

CHAPTER ELEVEN: GRATITUDE

CHAPTER TWELVE:
TOPICS FOR DISCUSSION AND JOURNALING

FOREWORD: WELCOME HOME!

A mong all stories of experience, strength, and hope shared by compulsive overeaters, one story, in particular, leapt from the pages of the first collection of *Lifeline* stories, *Lifeline Sampler*, and over the course of thirty years has found its way into the hearts of recovering compulsive eaters around the globe. Often read at the beginnings of meetings, "Welcome Home!" is a loving and unifying call to the newcomer, the longtimer, and to those working every intermediate Step on our journey.

Welcome Home!

H ave you ever wished you could lose ten pounds (5 kg)? Twenty (9 kg)? Forty (18 kg)? A hundred (45 kg) or more? Have you ever wished that once you got it off you could keep it off? Welcome to OA; welcome home!

Have you sometimes felt out of step with the world, like a homeless orphan without a place where you really belong? Welcome to OA; welcome home!

Have you ever wished your family would get to work or school so that you could get busy eating? Welcome to OA; welcome home!

Have you ever awakened first thing in the morning and felt happy because you remembered that your favorite goodie was waiting for you in the fridge or in the cupboard? Welcome to OA; welcome home!

Have you ever looked up at the stars and wondered what an insignificant person like you is doing in the world anyway? Welcome to OA; welcome home!

Have you ever cooked, bought, or baked for your family

and then eaten everything yourself so that you wouldn't have to share? We know you in OA because we are you. Welcome to OA; welcome home!

Have you ever wanted to hide in the house, without going to work, without getting cleaned up or even getting dressed, without seeing anyone or letting anyone see you? Welcome to OA; welcome home!

Have you ever hidden food under the bed, under the pillow, in the drawer, in the bathroom, in the wastebasket, the cupboard, the clothes hamper, the closet, or the car so that you could eat without anyone seeing you? Welcome to OA; welcome home!

Have you ever been angry, resentful, defiant—toward God, your mate, your doctor, your mother, your father, your friends, your children, the salespeople in stores whose looks spoke a thousand words as you tried on clothes—because they were thin, because they wanted you to be thin, and because you were forced to diet to please them or shut them up or make them eat their words and their looks? We welcome you to OA; welcome home!

Have you ever sobbed out your misery in the dark night because no one loved or understood you? Welcome to OA; welcome home!

Have you ever felt that God (if God existed at all) made the biggest mistake by creating you? Can you see that this is where such feelings get turned around? Welcome to OA; welcome home!

Have you ever wanted to get on a bus and just keep going, without ever once looking back? Or did you do it? Welcome to OA; welcome home!

Have you ever thought the whole world is a mess, and if they would just think and act like you, the world would be a lot better off? Welcome to OA; welcome home!

Have you ever thought that OA people must be a bit nuts?

That they might be compulsive overeaters, but you just have a weight problem that you can take care of beginning tomorrow; they might be one bite from insane eating, but you are just a little or a lot overweight? Welcome to OA; welcome home!

Have you ever told anyone who would listen how great you are, how talented, how intelligent, how powerful—all the time knowing they would never believe it, because you didn't believe it? Welcome to OA; welcome home!

Have you ever lost all your weight and then found that you were thin and unhappy instead of fat and unhappy? Welcome to OA; welcome home!

Have you ever worn a mask or hundreds of masks because you were sure that if you shared the person you really are no one could ever love or accept you? We accept you in OA. May we offer you a home?

Overeaters Anonymous extends to all of you the gift of acceptance. No matter who you are, where you come from, or where you are heading, you are welcome here! No matter what you have done or failed to do, what you have felt or haven't felt, where you have slept or with whom, who you have loved or hated—you may be sure of our acceptance. We accept you as you are, not as you would be if you could melt yourself and mold yourself and shape yourself into what other people think you should be. Only you can decide what you want to be.

But we will help you work for the goals you set, and when you are successful, we will rejoice with you; when you slip, we will tell you that we are not failures just because we sometimes fail, and we'll hold out our arms, in love, and stand beside you as you pull yourself back up and walk on again to where you are heading! You'll never have to cry alone again, unless you choose to.

Sometimes we fail to be all that we should be, and sometimes we aren't there to give you all you need from us. Accept our imperfection too. Love us in return and help us in our sometimes-falling failing. That's what we are in OA—imperfect, but trying. Let's rejoice together in our effort and in the assurance that we can have a home, if we want one.

Welcome to OA; welcome home!

—September/October 1977

1

NEWCOMERS

A Little Willingness

Today I was excited to take a ninety day coin at a meeting. This represents ninety days of complete abstinence from sugar and sweeteners of all kinds—something I didn't think possible. I haven't seen a huge weight loss yet, which has been trying, but I do have major health improvements and actually look forward to talking with my doctor about my blood tests.

I'd like to share with other newcomers a few things that have been working for me. First, a little willingness goes a long way. When I started, I was willing to go to only one meeting and listen. Then I was willing to go to another and take a welcome chip. A little at a time, I became willing to write down phone numbers and, later, to call some of those numbers. I became willing to make two meetings a week, then three; now I have two service commitments. If I had to do it all at once, I could never have done it. But because I was willing to go to just one meeting, miracles unfolded.

Second, I jumped into working the Steps right away. I believe this is not merely a diet plan, but a spiritual program that will help me learn how to live and restore my sanity. I've just completed a written First Step and am working on the Second Step. I don't know what the right pace or method is for anyone else, but I've had to take my time and do a thorough job. Writing a First Step has helped me see that I've been in crisis for a long time and no other plan has worked. No matter how hard I try, how educated I become, or how much I wish it were otherwise, I have a disease I can't control. That powerlessness is hard to face, but it leads to a real solution—one that works!

Finally, I can come to this solution only with the help of a Higher Power. I had what they call "the gift of desperation" after my doctor asked why I was killing myself with food. Not being able to answer, and alone in the exam room, I did something I had never done before: I got down on my knees to ask for help. A few weeks later, I attended my first OA meeting. The first week in OA I asked my Higher Power to help me figure out what my abstinence should be since I found that confusing. I received a quick and clear answer, along with the message I didn't have to get it perfect in my first week; I just had to keep coming back. One last thing: as repetitive as our phrases and slogans can be, darn if they don't turn out to be true. Progress, not perfection, and we don't have to do it alone!

—*March 2008*

Best Present Ever

I never had a weight issue until I delivered my second child. I had many stressors right after I delivered my daughter, including deaths in the family, issues within my marriage, a job loss, and a diagnosis of ADHD in my son. I also began to deal with the abuse I suffered as a child. I didn't lose my pregnancy weight and gained more. I was overeating, although I didn't know that term.

I wasn't aware of what I was doing, as crazy as that sounds. I just ate to cover up pain and fill my heart's gaping hole. I knew I wasn't happy, especially as my weight continued to rise. I had tried other diet plans, but nothing worked. What was I doing wrong?

I figured out I was overeating and was a sugar and caffeine addict. I had heard of OA somewhere along the line and looked it up on the computer. I was ready to go to a meeting when my husband said, "You don't need that. You just need to eat healthier and exercise more." I thought maybe he was right. I decided I was weak and undisciplined. I went through another year of overeating and beating myself up every day for not being strong enough and for being out of control. What was wrong with me?

Then in September I was visiting my parents, and my step-mother mentioned she had heard about OA and was going to a meeting. I told her I had heard about it and had almost gone a year ago. She was shocked and excited at the same time.

At my first meeting on September 5, 2012, I decided OA was the answer for me. At last I recognized the problem: I have a disease; I am an addict. Diets and self-pity won't help me. Only my Higher Power, the strength of others in this program, and the Steps will help me, day by day—sometimes minute by minute. I am so grateful.

I celebrated ninety days of abstinence on December 6, and getting the power and support I've always needed is the best present I've given myself in my life. Thank you, OA.

—June 2013

If I Can, You Can

I'm not a newcomer to OA—I've been coming to meetings for over a year—but I am a newcomer to abstinence. I've been abstinent for thirteen glorious days. Hallelujah! For thirteen days I've been waking up and going to bed surprised and grateful that God is doing for me what I cannot do for myself.

I didn't think the miracle would happen for me. I was terminally unique, or so I thought. I was fatter, sicker, and crazier than all of you. The program didn't, couldn't, wouldn't work for me. But desperation and the commitment I made to open a meeting once a week kept me coming back. That was the only thing I did right all those months: I kept coming back. I rarely picked up the OA Tools. Sometimes I did, but most of the time I didn't.

"How It Works" on page 58 in the Big Book (*Alcoholics Anonymous*, 4th ed.) told me I needed to be rigorously honest and willing to go to any length. I was neither. It told me I needed to be fearless and thorough from the very start. I was neither. It told me I needed to stop searching for an easier, softer way and to stop holding on to my old ideas. I did neither. Then after months of on-again, off-again prayer—more off than on, a miracle happened!

For thirteen days I have picked up the OA Tools and used them. For thirteen days I have been rigorously honest and willing to go to any length. For thirteen days I have been fearless and thorough. For thirteen days I have stopped searching for an easier, softer way, and I have stopped holding on to my old ideas. And for thirteen days I have been abstinent! Is this a coincidence? I think not.

The program works if I work it. It's that simple. If I want to hang on to my abstinence, I know what I need to do. Am I willing? You better believe it! Abstinence is even better than everyone says it is. Can you get abstinent? You better believe it! If I can do it, you can do it.

—April 2005

What a Week!

I have had an amazing first week in OA. I've gained a tiny insight into what it is to be "normal." It hasn't come without problems or temptations, but I can say I want to feel like this all the time.

The morning after my first OA meeting, for the first time

in ages, I didn't shop on the way to work. I would justify those trips—getting sugar for the tea and coffee club *and buying chocolate*, needing petrol *and two-for-one chocolates*, or buying baked goods for someone at work *and a muffin for me*. I must have spent at least $50 a week.

That day at work, I checked the drinks fund I'm in charge of. I had been borrowing money for the vending machine and justifying it by buying things for the club when I bought groceries, figuring it evened out. To my shock, $25 was missing—"borrowed" by me—so I repaid it. What a relief!

Next, I avoided an afternoon tea I had arranged for a guest speaker and a later event for which I had ordered my favorite goodies. Instead, I stayed at my desk.

The next test came when I went to visit Mum. I grabbed my wallet in case I might pass a shop, but realized I didn't need anything, so I left it at home. Mum always has something in the fridge for me. On my arrival, she announced it. "No thanks," I said to my surprise.

And that was all by the end of day one!

Bolstered by my first successful day, I found that the second wasn't so scary. I knew I could do this, one day at a time.

My biggest challenge was the supermarket. Before going in, I sat in my car and asked Higher Power for strength to bypass the temptations. The number I encountered amazed me! Now that I wasn't indulging, I was aware of the magnetic pull as I passed the bakery, donut shop, and confectionary aisle. I used to plan my shopping by what food stalls I wanted to visit and my drive home by what shops I would pass. Who knows how much petrol I wasted driving extra laps around back streets to finish my secret feast.

I did a final cleanout of my car and filled a shopping bag with wrappers. I felt wonderful, no longer fearing my husband might find one of my hiding spots. I relished arriving at work still tasting toothpaste in my mouth instead of whatever I had eaten.

At times this week, I felt so on top of my game I almost thought I had imagined my problems. But I've experienced this bulletproof feeling before, only to fall hard when things got out of hand again.

It's a great relief to admit I'm out of control and need help from a Higher Power. It takes away the guilt of failing so often before. I had judged success or failure by the number I saw on the scale. Not this time! How liberating to realize my journey is about getting my mind healthy and that my body will eventually reflect the changes I make. Now I know I'm on track and will be where I'm supposed to be when I'm supposed to get there.

All I can do is live the best I can, day by day, with the constant presence of mind that something greater than myself is looking after me.

—December 2008

What a Relief!

Outsiders think we addicts white knuckle abstinence from our drugs of choice, one day at a time. Many people have the misconception that's all a Twelve Step program entails. It's true that we don't have to worry about avoiding compulsive eating for weeks, months, years, or forever, but just for today. But "one day at a time" means so much more than that.

I've been in OA for six weeks. I've been on the planet for sixty years, and I could have benefited from the program for at least forty of them. But that kind of thinking is no more one-day-at-a-time than is worrying about Step Nine when I'm just embarking on Step Three. This is my path. I can't regret that I didn't walk this way decades ago; I can only keep putting one foot in front of the other now.

My relationship with a Higher Power is of paramount interest to me at this time of my life. It's been an itch for a while, and the lucky timing of a phone conversation brought me to an OA meeting. I'm finding the tools to scratch that itch as I continue to work the program, day by day.

I had many doubts early on. I feared that my compulsion was different, stronger than others', and that I would fail as I had in the past with mere physical tools. I was living in the future rather than day by day. And I was self-centered; I felt I must somehow be different. I am different and special—not because these Tools, properly used, won't work for me, but because they will. We are all special, and we are blessed to have the privilege of straightening out our lives and our relationships with people and a Higher Power.

Right now, "one day at a time" means I see progress. I'm in a different place than I was two, four, or six weeks ago. I can trust the process and not worry whether I'll master it. Daily activity will get the job done. Trying to control the future is fruitless and wastes the energy I need to work my program today.

That's the gift of one day at a time: We don't have to control everything all the time. What a relief! We need to focus on the assignment at hand and change what we can. We can only change tomorrow by working today.

—May 2009

Cold Fresh Air

When I came to OA six weeks ago, I was ready to admit defeat. After an early life of somewhat normal eating, I started compulsive overeating after the birth of my second child. I was stuck in a spiral of hopelessness and depression. At 5 feet 3 inches (160 cm), I weighed 185 pounds (84 kg) and barely had the physical or spiritual energy to get out of bed, much less face the day. When I experienced repeated failure at dieting and began sneaking food, isolating myself to eat, and resenting the normal eaters around me, I knew I needed help.

That first OA meeting was like taking a breath of painfully cold fresh air. Though I was terrified to face daily life without the comfort of my food, the possibility of freedom from overeating and the promise of a useful, peaceful life were more compelling.

I worked with my sponsor, and Step One seemed easy since I had tried everything to control my eating before coming to OA. But as I moved through Step Two and into Step Three, I felt myself changing, becoming honest with myself for the first time about the true nature of my food obsession.

The longer I am abstinent, the more committed I am to turning over my issues, food and otherwise, to my Higher Power every day. As my mind clears from its haze of food, it feels good to clarify the terms of my abstinence and continue to refine my plan of eating, so my food can become fuel and I can be at peace.

After forty days of abstinence, I have lost 14 pounds (6 kg) and am starting to remember how it feels to have a healthy body that can make it through the day without an aching fatigue. Every day of abstinence helps me understand why I need to be fearless and searching as I make the slow way through my Step work.

In the beginning I was scared to start, but now I'm scared to stop. And I couldn't be more grateful.

—July 2009

New Possibilities

Before I stepped into the OA rooms sixty-one days ago, I was hopeless. I had lost hope of ever living in a body I could be proud of and comfortable with. I told God many times it would be better if he would let me die rather than live in this body. I had lost hope of getting ahold of the eating behaviors ruining my life.

Before experiencing an OA meeting, it never occurred to me I could abstain from chronic late-night binges for weeks, months, or even years. When I stepped into the OA rooms and discovered people who had gone decades without bingeing, my eyes opened to new possibilities. I found a sponsor by my third OA meeting. Within two weeks, I purchased and began reading the OA literature my sponsor recommended.

For the past sixty-one days, I've averaged five to six meetings a week, sometimes going to two meetings a day. I took advantage of the two complimentary *Lifeline* issues in my *Newcomer Packet* and plan to purchase a subscription. I call my sponsor every weekday. I make and take outreach calls and volunteer to call newcomers at meetings. I am willing to hand over my will and life to my Higher Power's care. At one of my meetings, I took a service commitment. I speak when members ask me to lead a meeting. I'm only sixty days into my recovery, and an entire world has opened up for me.

I now inhabit a body that feels and looks good. I get dressed, give myself a once-over in the mirror, and am out the door. I no longer feel the need to scrutinize, fidget, and lament over how my clothes are or aren't fitting. It feels good to wake up with an empty stomach instead of the lethargic sense of having injected myself with a vat of poison.

The highlight of my day used to be curling up at night to a favorite TV show with my bag or box of poison, stuffing my face, and living vicariously through the characters onscreen. I was too busy not living my life because I felt so uncomfortable in my body. Now I'm present. Now my day's highlights are when I'm out and about, living and achieving my dreams and connecting with people within and outside of program.

I have a freedom I didn't know I'd experience so soon. I am grateful.

—*December 2010*

After the Fear

My life before OA was empty. I sought but seldom found God, relationships, and happiness. I was an only (lonely) child, and my alone time increased after my parents' divorce. My alcoholic dad was often absent. Mom worked full time, leaving me with the TV for company and the kitchen for comfort. Making friends was hard; I wasn't relaxed or easygoing. Food was my friend.

With mom's help, I went on my first diet at age 11. Mom tried every diet fad or club, with a long binge in between. I followed her model for eating if you're bored, lonely, angry, tired, happy, celebrating, sad, depressed, or socializing.

Before OA, I thought I was in control. I had a wonderful husband, a beautiful child, a comfortable and safe home, an education, financial security, friends, freedom, and opportunities. But I felt guilty, and I wasn't happy. I thought only of food.

I stressed over decisions and took everything personally, feeling attacked, misunderstood, unappreciated, and taken advantage of. I didn't trust or like most people; they didn't seem to value me as I thought they should. If friends or family didn't put my needs first, then something was wrong with them.

I was dishonest, not telling people, God, or even myself the truth about me. If I didn't like part of me and couldn't easily change it, I changed my values about it. I sank into a valueless oblivion, eating to escape life and feelings.

In recent years, I spent much time isolating in bed, watching TV, and eating. I wondered how actors stayed so thin and watched diet commercials with disdain, knowing the products didn't work. I was a worthless wife and mother and wondered why my husband didn't leave me, why my friends didn't call, how I'd gotten so fat, and what I could eat. When I was willing to leave the house, I left only for food. Holidays were an excuse to buy or bake my favorite sweets. Guilt came over what and how much I had eaten. I ate to feel better.

Two things changed: I became aware of my disease's progression, not knowing its name, and I moved to Placerville, California USA, where I couldn't isolate because my mother-in-law lives next door.

I was reading OA meeting ads in the newspaper—God's intervention—but would go back to bed thinking anything with "anonymous" was for losers.

The progression of my disease became more severe. I was ill, selfish, far away from God's plan, and hurtful to everyone. At the bottom of a deep pit, I had no idea how I got there or how to get out.

One evening in bed, I finished my third fat-filled snack and wondered if there was more. God intervened, ringing in my ears, "Why can't I stop?" I knew then I was beyond my own help and was willing to do anything.

Freaked out, I went to an OA meeting. I don't remember what was said, but I remember my feelings. The new vocabulary and ideas confused me. I was unsure whether I belonged, but the honesty I heard amazed me. I decided to return, if only to hear more. I became more comfortable at the next meeting.

I bought the *Twelve and Twelve* after my first meeting, drank it in, and carried it everywhere. I attended a month of meetings before getting a sponsor and became willing to do whatever members told me to do to find recovery. I read OA books in parking lots, waiting rooms, parks, and fast-food-restaurant play areas.

Fear was my biggest obstacle to working the Steps. I learned to trust God by using baby steps. He came through on the little stuff, so I figured I could trust him with the big stuff. After sharing my Fifth Step with my sponsor, I felt freedom I had never known. Sanity began.

Today my days begin with the Third Step Prayer (*Alcoholics Anonymous,* 4th ed., p. 63) and end with a Tenth Step inventory. I focus on program and God's will. If I don't, they will take a backseat to my emotions, self-will, and all else.

Today I am sane and serene. I don't worry about my food, weight, people, or needs being met. I entrust all to God's care, listening for him to say where I can serve him and others. I set aside time for worship, devotion, and self-care through yoga and therapy. I deal with my addiction by attending meetings, calling my sponsor daily, and working the Steps. I trust, love, and honor people and make amends when necessary. The extra 50 pounds (23 kg) took care of itself. My trigger foods look like poison. I have seven months of abstinence, and I feel happy and purposeful.

—January 2011

Away from the Edge

Today is my sixty-fifth day in OA, but it seems more like six months, or even years, since I came to OA because I have found so much and my life is so different.

When I came to OA, I knew I had a big problem. I had been overweight for thirty-eight years and tried every diet. I attended two thirty-day retreats and lost 30 pounds (14 kg), only to gain 40 pounds (18 kg) three years later. I cut out this and that but slowly worked myself up to 80 pounds (36 kg) overweight. I had four-vessel bypass surgery, a stent, and close calls with death. But I still couldn't take off the weight.

Despite all this, when I heard, "I am a compulsive overeater and powerless over food," I thought, "I'm not a big eater. I don't gorge myself. I'm thoughtful about meals. This is not me." Then one night, four days into OA, it occurred to me: It's true. I eat three good meals a day, but the fourth meal from 9 p.m. to midnight is a killer. When I thought about my life post 9 p.m., I knew I was a compulsive overeater, powerless over food. I knew I was home at OA.

Members said to attend at least six meetings and try different ones, so I did. I read the *Newcomer Packet* pamphlets and OA's *Twelve and Twelve*. I understood the concept of surrender to a Higher Power and that I alone could not cure my illness.

My sponsor said, "Don't stay on the edge; it's too easy to fall off. Immerse yourself in program. Get involved. Service is so important, and reading and writing make all the difference." Bless him; that guidance has meant so much! Now I have a new life with new friends and a wonderful sponsor who guides and inspires me.

Now I read and pray every morning before my feet hit the floor. I reach out to my Higher Power—my version of a loving, nonjudgmental Higher Power—asking for guidance. I stop during my day to take deep breaths to calm my mind. I close my eyes to express gratitude for my Higher Power, sponsor, OA's *Twelve and Twelve,* and the OA community that accepts and supports me.

I've been abstinent on and off five times in my sixty-five days, but I take it one day at a time. It takes time to release old habits, establish a strong connection with my Higher Power, and let go of trying to do it all myself. But I'm getting closer and lifted up each day. Now that I understand I am not in control, life is different. I don't need to be in control of my life, my wife's life, my children's lives, or anyone's life. I just let go and let God, and I am getting better at it one day at a time. Thank you, OA and my Higher Power.

—May 2012

Hope for Next Year

I walked into my first OA meeting in 2011. I had done research prior to the meeting, so I thought I knew what to expect.

I was 48, married, and employed, but most important, I was obsessed with food. Compulsive overeating is a progressive disease; that is true in my case. It hit me hard and heavy the two years before that meeting. If I was awake, I was thinking of food. I looked forward to bedtime so I could get up in the morning to leave the house to eat. I was a secret eater. If I was alone, chances were, I was eating.

When I came to OA, I was 40 pounds (18 kg) overweight, 10 pounds (5 kg) below my top weight of 214 pounds (97 kg). I could not stay on a diet for more than a couple of hours, was miserable, and knew something was wrong, but I had no idea what. I had tried the diets, diet pills, and programs, just like everyone else, and thought my next step would be the psychiatrist's office.

I didn't know anything about OA except what I had heard in a radio ad years before. Thanks to the Internet, I found all I needed to know. I was a compulsive overeater, and hope existed that I could have some relief from the disease. I could not wait to get to an OA meeting. After the meeting, I realized I had found my people. Nobody can give hugs better than a room full of compulsive overeaters.

My life started to change right away. I found abstinence, serenity, and relief from the food obsession. And I was lucky that I began to do service right away because it has helped me a lot and I enjoy it.

The real transformation began at my first retreat. I could feel the recovery in the room. I had issues I had to work on before I could continue my recovery. The ladies loved and supported me through my tears. I could not have done this alone.

After the retreat, I was able to set boundaries I had neglected and work through feelings I had held in. I found serenity. It is awesome! I found a sponsor, who is my constant support. The sponsor/sponsee relationship is very important, and working this program without a sponsor might result in failure.

So many good things have happened to me—and a few not-so-good things. It is a miracle I got through the latter without eating about them.

People have noticed changes in me, not just that I have lost twenty pounds (9 kg), but that I have changed on the inside, thanks to my HP, this program, and the Tools it offers. I hope when next year comes around, I will still have the excitement, love, and passion for my program I have today.

—*September 2013*

2

STEPS ONE TO THREE

Step One Situation

S ince I have been in program, I have struggled with abstinence a few times, but most days I am blessed with a solid abstinence. Most of this is because of the support of working the OA Twelve Step program to the best of my ability. I rely on Twelve Step literature. My literature often has kept me aware, so that I don't binge.

During my sixteen years in OA, of all of the Steps I've experienced, Step One has played a huge role in maintaining my abstinence. "We admitted we were powerless over food—that our lives had become unmanageable." Writing this inspires me!

I am powerless over more than just food in my life. I am powerless over how things happen at work, over the behavior of family and friends, over how our pets act. Before I walked into these rooms, I would behave unladylike with my choice of words and actions; often I would binge and overeat my many trigger foods.

Today when I find my life in a Step One situation, I find the true blessing of OA. I don't have to choose to binge, use a laxative, or compulsively overeat. I can feel what may be an unhappy part of my life and deal with it to make it better. I do this by using my Twelve Step literature, admitting I am powerless over the situation, and taking care of myself. How? I eat healthier food. I may go to a face-to-face or telephone meeting. Perhaps I share with my sponsor, with my sponsee, or on an online OA loop. Until I recognize, accept, and admit that the situation is Step One and I am powerless, I cannot act. My blessing is that I no longer need to eat over it. By working Step One in many aspects of life, I keep my abstinence intact.

As far as keeping my abstinence with a support system, that would be my sponsor, sponsees, other OA members, family, and friends. My daughter, granddaughters, husband, son, music teacher, and many coworkers have often encouraged me not to give up through the years. They remind me how much I work my program when I am in a "normal" state of mind. They encourage me by letting me know that often my strength has kept them going in different situations. I am often inspired by their patience or when they hand me my Twelve Step books, be it a *Lifeline* magazine or the Big Book.

Without Step One and the support of all these people in my life, in honesty, I am not sure I would have the abstinence that has blessed me for these sixteen years in the OA program.

—January 2013

Powerless Perspective

A dictionary definition of the word "powerless" is "helpless, without authority."

On my own, I was and am helpless, without the authority needed to make changes in my relationship with food. Most of us have been able to imagine we were powerful over food, for a time, because our addiction to diets worked early in our food experience, giving us the illusion of control. Then one day, they didn't work anymore. No matter how strong our willpower, and I believe most of us demonstrate extraordinary willpower, we could no longer will ourselves to lose weight or keep it off for long. When I reached that stage, I was sure my willpower was the problem.

When I finally came to OA, after six successful years in AA, I began to realize that food had always been my primary addiction, present since early childhood. But I still did not see my own powerlessness over food and compulsive food behaviors. At that time, food consumed most of my waking hours: planning, shopping, learning new recipes, cooking, eating, and using just the right containers for cooking and storing my precious food.

I learned from my group that I needed a new approach to life. I learned also that to retake authority over my life, I had to admit my powerlessness over most of life and its events. I began to gain an understanding of my helplessness over my disease of compulsive eating, first on an intellectual and later on an emotional level. It felt as I imagined bankruptcy would feel—an experience I had narrowly escaped several times because of my addiction to overspending—like reaching the end of life as I knew it. At that time, it was an experience for me of utter humiliation and defeat.

By working the OA program with the help of my sponsor and doing the Steps as suggested in OA's *Twelve and Twelve* and the workbook, which really spoke to me, I began to move from defeat to an understanding of my own inevitable limitedness. I am only a human being. All past feelings of power over life, others, and food began to transform into acceptance and humility.

—January 2013

Not Normal, But Free

For years I thought of myself as abnormal. My compulsive overeating had brought me down to the dust. I felt ashamed, isolated, and unlovable.

Only when I finally admitted my powerlessness over food and came to believe deep in my heart that I was not sane around food did I find relief. Only when I surrendered my self-will did God free me of my compulsion to binge and purge.

Incredibly, when I recognized my abnormal reaction to food, my life improved. Not only did God free me of the compulsion to binge and purge, but I also became more open to the people and activities around me. I turned outward toward others instead of inward away from them.

With food in its proper place, I can enjoy life and be a part of it. I will never be a "normal" eater, but with God's help and OA's support I can be an abstinent one. Thank you, God. Thank you, OA.

—January 2012

My Shepherd

My idea of a Higher Power changes all the time. It went from the "God in the sky" of my childhood religion to atheism. When I came into the Twelve Step program, I "acted as if" there was a Higher Power. Eventually, I came to believe in God as a loving energy within me and within each person. This concept of God makes me feel connected in love to others and myself.

Today in meditation, it came to me that what I need and want in a Higher Power is a being who loves me, takes care of me, and gives me affection. I pictured myself as a trusting dog, taken care of and petted with love the way I take care of my dog!

This brought to mind an OA speaker I heard years ago. She said her relationship with her Higher Power was like that of a shepherd and his sheep. The speaker explained that in general sheep are dumb animals that need to be watched and guided many times to do what is necessary for their survival and well-being. I can identify with that concept.

So, as smart and independent as I often think I am, sometimes I am like a sheep or a dog that needs a loving, guiding force to take care of me and shower me with affection.

—December 2009

Rainbow of Colors

After seven and a half years in program and over four years of back-to-back abstinence, I find myself struggling to describe my Higher Power. I have one or many or something, but what is it? It was easier when I believed in something called God. He was clear and simple to define as Higher Power, and my religion told me all about him. I didn't have to figure out much for myself. This God worked well for me when I first came into recovery. Getting abstinent is hard enough without figuring out the whole Higher Power thing.

As I've grown in recovery, I've gotten to know myself better. I gave myself permission to view my Higher Power with a critical eye and found the God of my childhood lacking. A more freethinking, atheist philosophy feels honest and comfortable for me. I am happy with the change and don't miss God. The only drawback is I no longer have a pat answer to the question "What is Higher Power to me?" This seems to be a theme in my life. What was once black and white is now a rainbow of colors.

I prefer the phrase "power greater than myself" to Higher Power. "Higher" implies the power is better than me, while "greater" means bigger. This idea fits better with my world view; I see everything as equal and nothing is above or below. I am no more special than a rock, just different. When I think this way, I can see that many forces are more powerful than I. The natural world provides plenty of examples: gravity, evolution, birth, and death, to name a few. Certain laws of nature govern these and all other processes of life. I am subject to these natural laws; accepting this reality aligns me with this power.

When I accept life on life's terms, things flow better. I put my energy into things I can affect (my thoughts and actions) and leave the rest to the process of life.

The collective power of the program is a power greater than myself. I don't see it as God-given as many do, but I do see it is an effective process. Connecting with others, being honest about my motives, helping people, and having self-reflection and quiet time are tremendous tools for living a useful and fulfilling life. The program isn't perfect, but it doesn't need to be. I am happier when I use it, so I continue to do so.

Love is a wonderful power greater than myself. When I do my best to love others and myself, things work better. I am happier and so are others.

The concept of Higher Power is a deeply personal one, and OA has room for all interpretations. I would hate for someone to miss out on recovery because he or she didn't agree with the general concept of God. I share my experience with the God issue because I want all to feel welcome. I love walking this path with each and every one of you.

—*December 2009*

I Love Step Two

I grew up in a family that attended church every week. I went to religious schools and felt that my family and teachers shoved religion down my throat and did not tolerate questions and doubts. Yet at home, my family did not take faith seriously. I grew up thinking people who believed were stupid and weak.

I walked into my first OA meeting at age 15 on March 22, 1977, intending to lose 20 pounds (9 kg). I remember hearing Step Three about a God *as we understood Him*. Never before had anyone told me I could develop my concept of God. Those words opened my mind for the first time.

While I was working on Step Two, I asked program people to describe their Higher Powers, and I soaked in the many perspectives. I also began to make an honest search. I discovered faith in a loving being who wanted very much what was best for me. My Higher Power reached me at the level of my needs. At the time, disco was at its height, and I would go to the clubs with my friends, feeling fat and ugly. In the pounding music and swirling lights, I could sense my Higher Power's presence, as if he loved me so much he was coming to find me where I was. I began to feel loved and worthy from the inside out, and my intense self-hate began to disappear.

On January 17, 1980, after almost three years of struggle, I got abstinent and then lost 30 pounds (14 kg). My spiritual journey continued, but after a few years, I wanted to search beyond program literature. I began to explore the faith of my childhood with fresh eyes and an open mind. I discovered that my traditional religion reflected much of what I found in program. I returned to Christianity, although not to the denomination of my youth.

Instead I found a more loving and gentle place that welcomed questions, doubts, and other viewpoints. Today my Christian faith and my program work hand-in-hand, and I am grateful for my continuing spiritual journey. I have many friends with different beliefs, and I think my Higher Power is like a stunning crystal, reflecting light and color in different and beautiful ways, depending on how we receive it.

I do not understand everything about my Higher Power nor do I claim to have all the answers. All I know is that when I became honest, open minded, and willing, something loving and kind reached down and removed a deadly addiction that no amount of my willpower or effort could erase. I love Step Two.

—June 2013

Best Decision

Addicts who are active in their addiction dislike facing reality. I know because I was active in my addiction for thirty-five years. I hid behind a wall of isolation and beneath vast amounts of my drug of choice: excess food. I did not want any part of reality.

What changed for me? We all have our bottoms, and I hit mine at the age of 50. I lost my job and could not find another. No one wanted to hire a 300-pound (136-kg) woman with a high school education, even if she had years of experience. I spent a year looking for work and finally had to take another type of position.

During that year, I remembered OA and thought of looking online for help. I had joined OA for a year in the mid-1980s, but my fear and self-will kept me from committing to the program. However, I remembered OA was there if and when I wanted it. I went back, and this time I was much more willing to work the program. I found an online OA support group, joined their Step study, and got a sponsor.

It still took me two and a half years of working program before I accepted the reality of being a compulsive overeater. I did not want to be an addict or have to work program. I wanted what I wanted, when I wanted it, and in whatever amounts I wanted. I would work only the parts of program that appealed to me, the parts I found safe and comfortable.

Working program part-time gave me only partial recovery, but it increased my awareness of what my disease was doing to me. I was breaking down the denial I had hidden beneath for so long. The more aware I was of the disease, the less was my denial. Then came the day when I accepted the truth.

I am an addict whether I want to be or not. I am an addict whether I work program or not, whether I am abstinent or not, and whether I am in recovery or not. I can be an addict in recovery, or I can be an addict in hell. I choose to be an addict in recovery. Once I broke through the denial, I had nothing left but the truth.

I chose to be an addict in recovery at Step Three. I decided to turn my addiction and my life over to the care of my Higher Power. On June 1, 2004, I made my decision and began my recovery in the Twelve Step program of Overeaters Anonymous. It is the best decision I have ever made.

—January 2011

Recovery in My Heart

I first came to OA at age 22. About four months before going to my first meeting, I had started outpatient treatment for anorexia and bulimia. At an eating disorders workshop, I met a beautiful woman who told her story of recovery with many parts similar to mine. We talked after the workshop, and she gave me a schedule of OA meetings.

The schedule had a list of OA members in recovery who were willing to take phone calls. The first person listed was not home. The second person was like an angel; she, too, was in recovery from anorexia and bulimia and was so understanding and compassionate that I asked her to be my sponsor. In my first few months, I listened and learned much from my sponsor and new OA friends. I started working the Steps and using the Tools, especially writing and telephone. Physical abstinence from my disease happened right away.

It didn't take much longer before I had my first spiritual experience. I was in tears while at a beach restroom changing into my bikini. By medical standards, I was a few pounds under the normal weight for my age and height, but all I saw in the mirror was a fat person. My best friend hugged me and insisted I looked beautiful. I thanked her and told her I'd meet her and our friends outside. I retreated into the bathroom stall, locked the door, and prayed. After praying I took deep breaths and joined my friends.

We splashed in the water, and I felt as if the waves had taken away my self-consciousness and horrible thoughts of myself. Was God doing for me what I could not do myself? I was having fun and enjoying the feel of the water on my body and the company of friends. That was the first time I understood what it meant to let go and let God.

Over the years I focused on my life in mind, body, and

spirit. When I worked on spiritual fitness, everything else seemed to fall into place. I finished college, quit a job that was unsuitable for my personality, and found meaningful work. Gone were unhealthy relationships with men. God and program helped me through my mother's stroke and heart attack. During adverse times, it became natural for me to practice healthy recovery behaviors rather than past anorexic or bulimic behaviors.

Through OA, recovery came into my heart. I will be 27 soon and will mark five years in recovery. I carry OA's message through sharing my story at meetings and sponsoring. Eating disorders that almost killed me gave me the opportunity to live a life of love, serenity, abundance, and peace. Each day is a gift, and each day I aspire to be an instrument of God's love and peace. When that doesn't work, I have the Steps and Tools to help me find my way back. I never feel alone. Thank God for the beautiful gifts of love and life OA has given me.

—March/April 2006

My "Aha!" Step

Step Three has given me the greatest strength and has helped me the most with compulsive overeating. I have always been spiritual, and whenever I prayed and became open to God, my life at that time became bearable. However, I have also wanted to control every situation I encountered as well as people around me; I wanted to control God and how he worked. I was aware of the peace and power of a Higher Power, but I just couldn't let go of control. My life was manageable, but I was lonely and unhappy most of the time. I know now that I made close friends and relatives miserable by wanting to control their lives, but I was not aware that I was a controlling person until I worked the Steps.

I now start each day in prayer, asking for God's will for me and the strength and courage to carry it out. It seems simple, but when I let go and turn the day over to God, my day goes smoothly, and I feel happy. I appreciate my family, friends, and coworkers. My attitude has changed. I don't need to control how other people live their lives, and I don't have to do things I don't want to do to impress others or be liked.

By being an instrument of God, I have found a new freedom and happiness I never knew existed. I have been blessed to release 50 pounds (23 kg) through this wonderful program. I have more energy and strength to do God's will lovingly, one day at a time.

—March/April 2006

Turning It Over

When I first walked into OA, my Higher Power was far different from my HP of today. As a godly man, I thought I understood Step Three. The God of my understanding was a God who loved and cared about me, but small matters in my life were up to me to deal with. I would go to my HP for help and guidance with only the big things in life.

Initially, I thought my problem with food was a small matter of self-determination, and my willpower should be able to deal with it. Even people in my church tried to convince me all I needed was a little willpower to overcome this problem. I came to believe that what they were saying was true. Because I still struggled with my food, I must have something wrong with me, or I needed more willpower. In fact, I was powerless over food.

Then came Step Two, believing in a power greater than myself that could restore me to sanity. Me, insane? I don't believe it! Eventually I realized I did some crazy and insane things. I was faced with a dilemma. I had to find a new understanding of my HP.

I had to do some soul-searching; I prayed and meditated with the HP I understood and asked him for help with my food problem and my life. After a period of time, HP said, "Yes, I am the HP who will help you recover from your disease of compulsive overeating and will help you in all areas of your life." I finally realized my current understanding of God was far different from the God I believed in before OA. This new God filled my heart with amazing serenity and peace.

If I wanted to experience threefold recovery, this new HP would be the one to help me. What a blessing! I could trust this HP to help me find complete recovery from my disease and help me in all areas of my life!

Now I was ready to take Step Three. I could say the Third Step Prayer (*Alcoholics Anonymous*, 4th ed., p. 63) with full confidence in this new God of my understanding and let him be in charge. The miracles of this program started to become a reality!

One day at a time, I make this conscious decision to trust my HP with my life. My emotions are more balanced. I have received emotional and spiritual growth along with physical recovery.

Now I worry less about tomorrow and trust my HP. I believe this is what emotional abstinence is all about!

—December 2013

Morning Reboot

I love using analogies to help me better understand my life, compulsive overeating, and recovery in OA.

I used to struggle to remember that I've turned my will and life over to my Higher Power. Some days I would slip back into trying to control my life (and usually a couple of other people's lives too). When I realized what was happening, I stopped and said the Third Step Prayer (*Alcoholics Anonymous*, 4th ed., p. 63), or in some way returned my will and life to HP. The situation and the rest of my day would then go better.

I found this repeated slipping very frustrating. Hadn't I turned my will and life over to my Higher Power? Or was I just kidding myself? I paid attention to how it happened, and I concluded that when I woke up, I was automatically operating in "I am in charge" mode instead of "HP is in charge" mode. If I spent more time saying the Third Step Prayer (*Alcoholics Anonymous*, 4th ed., p. 63), reading OA literature, journaling, or meditating, I found myself back in "HP is in charge" mode. Since I'm not a patient person, I wondered why this should be necessary. Why wasn't it enough to turn my will and life over to HP once and for all?

Then one day I thought about my computer. When I reboot my computer, it starts up with a blank desktop. It's not very useful until I start running a couple of programs I regularly use. Suddenly it hit me! When I wake up each morning, it's like I was just rebooted. My "desktop" is my "I am in charge" mode. If I don't run a couple of "recovery programs" each morning, then I go through my day not being very useful to HP, others, or myself.

I don't waste time being frustrated that my computer boots up to a blank desktop; I just get those useful programs running as soon as possible. Likewise, I don't need to waste time wondering why my morning recovery routine is necessary. I just need to do it and move on with my day. For today, I accept that this is the way I operate and thank my HP that I now know what I need to do to get my day started right.

—July 2009

3

STEPS FOUR TO NINE

Uncovering

It all begins with a problem,
You know—a problem that plants itself,
Overtaking all thoughts,
Like a thick, permeating ivy
That the sun won't shine through,

Until you uncover the cause of the problem,
The person, place, or thing,
A statement, a behavior,
An institution's policies or procedures,
A resentment relived.

Whatever the cause,
You dig until you discover how you are affected,
Battered self-worth,
Emotional and physical security,
Rocked.

Writing is the Tool
That chips away at denial,
So that we see our part,
Our part in the problems,
Our part in the causes.

Underneath the problem
And the cause
And our part in it,
Lay those character defects,
Defenses built up in a lifetime,

Perfectionism and procrastination,
Denial and avoidance,
Pessimism and being judgmental,
People-pleasing and self-centeredness.
A moral inventory

Taken in Step Four,
Because we have taken Step Three,
And are willing to do what we need to do
To uncover, discover,
And recover.

—*March/April 2011*

God Is Bigger than My Fears

I recently took my Fifth Step with my sponsor. Driving home, I felt an elated sense of freedom and joy. I felt clean and lighter. It was as if a weight had been lifted off my body. I shared out loud with my sponsor things I had never admitted to another person.

Why had I been so nervous about this? Where did I get my fear of the Fourth and Fifth Steps? I am rather new to OA. I had never heard of the Steps or Traditions before. If someone were to ask me what Step Eight is, my response would be, "I don't know; I haven't taken that one yet." On the drive back to my house, I realized much of my fear came from fellow compulsive overeaters sharing their reservations and anxieties about these Steps. Some described the work as painful; others admitted to dragging their feet about doing Step Four.

Writing about some of my past was painful and difficult. I visited seasons of my life I've not talked about or acknowledged for years. But the Fifth Step was anything but painful; it was liberating! Sharing with God and my sponsor the exact nature of my wrongs was simply an exercise in honesty, something my disease says will bring consequences. The opposite is true. Instead of something bad happening as a result of admitting my wrongs, I was blessed with a reminder that God is bigger than my faults and more powerful than my fears or this disease of compulsive overeating.

The second blessing I received that day was a sense of hope; I don't have to fear my past and can overcome fears about the future. In this case, the truth about my past sets me free from the grip of my disease.

The book *Alcoholics Anonymous* suggests "taking" the Steps. I have yet to read "working the Steps" or "fearing the Steps" anywhere in the Big Book. Taking Steps Four and Five was an incredibly positive experience for me.

Today I have six months of abstinence and a renewed sense of hope. Both come from taking the Steps. I am excited to move forward with the Steps because they are such a powerful part of how I find recovery in this program. From this recent experience, I know I don't have to be nervous or fearful about the next Steps. I am taking the Steps Big Book style and am grateful for this journey to recovery.

—May 2006

Smooth Sailing

I learned about my character defects many years ago while working Steps Six and Seven. The Big Book has only a paragraph on these two Steps and does not go into great detail on how to work these important Steps. So I have tried many ways. One way was listing my character defects and looking them up in the dictionary. I listed the defect and the opposite of that word, so I could see what the opposite of my defect should be. But Steps Six and Seven really made sense to me when I made each *defect* a *character*; I imagined that my body was a pirate ship.

On this ship live my many characters, defects as well as good traits, but characters just the same. Everyone onboard wants to be the captain of my ship. To give you an example of the chaos I run into, I must introduce you to a few of my characters: Meet Picky Paul, the perfectionist; Schlep, the procrastinator; Stella, the organizer; Chip, resentment; Sister Mary Crap, guilt; Wally, fear; Mona, worry; and Divinity, in recovery. I have many more, but this gives an idea of the cast of characters that I am dealing with on my ship.

Some of them get along quite well, like Picky Paul and Stella, who both love to organize. But these two don't like Schlep, who likes to put things off until another day, or another year. Wally and Mona are great friends because worry and fear go hand in hand in my life. But they are terrified of divinity, because when she is in charge of the ship, they don't get to be captain. With these characters guiding my life and everyone onboard fighting to be in charge, it is no wonder my ship doesn't always sail well or go anywhere except in circles.

How do I get my characters in harmony with each other? I can't! But when the ultimate captain is running my ship, everyone gets along. My characters know they are important in my life, and all have moments of glory. When God is the captain of my ship, they all know everything is being taken care of. No single character has to have control because God is the ultimate captain and harmony prevails on my ship. God assigns every character a healthy duty to perform, and everyone is too busy to worry about other characters.

So when God is sailing my ship, we go to great places in

the world and have smooth sailing. Every day is an adventure, and all my characters are happy! But I must admit that my characters get out of hand some days, and we have mutiny on the ship. Those are the days I must remember to turn to God in Step Seven and ask him for help. I humbly ask him to straighten out my "defects of character," and we go back to smooth sailing—God, my characters, and me.

—December 2012

I Am Ready

I worked with God to create my Fourth Step inventory. Through hard work, I took an honest look at my resentments, fears, and relationships. After preparing the inventory, I scheduled time to review it with my sponsor. The effort of scheduling the face-to-face meeting, sitting down, opening my notes, and reading the work I'd done put me on the path to healing.

My recent Fifth Step surprised me. Six weeks later, I couldn't believe how much fear had built up inside me.

The Big Book tells me my next action is to approach Step Six. I see Step Six as a preparation task. I am almost there. With Higher Power's help, we can build "an arch through which we shall walk a free man at last" (*Alcoholics Anonymous*, 4th ed., p. 75). This means my fears, resentments, and self-seeking and selfish behaviors bind and keep me from a nourishing relationship with my Higher Power. I know what that binding is—I withdraw, I don't put myself out there to interact with others, and I descend into loneliness. And guess what? My disease is waiting for these low points!

I am ready to be free of resentment and fear. I want peace.

After I meditate, I leave nothing out of the inventory I share with my sponsor. I am ready.

My fears have not benefitted anyone, including me. They cause my heart to race, and I shut down and isolate. Yes, God, I am ready.

My self-seeking behaviors have not benefitted anyone either. Now I stay focused on others. Resentments build because life does not go where I want it to go. Yes, God, I am ready.

As in my morning meditation, I can look at Step Six as a wonderful transition opportunity. I can see the change beyond the arch. I just have to ask.

—June 2010

God-Testing

I have much to learn about the process of humbly asking God to remove my shortcomings. Each time I ask, I receive an answer I become aware of only in retrospect.

I've learned "humbly asking" means several things. I have to give up self-reliance. I am not the one who will do the removing, and it will not be done in my time frame or according to my methods (most of which are too comfortable to be effective anyway). In practice, it means I must ask God to present me with people, places, or things as a constant test of my ability to release my character defects. If my character defect is impatience, then I ask God to give me situations designed to test my patience and to give me the opportunity to find new ways of reacting with tolerance. My only choices are to stay in the misery or grow out of it.

God-testing is not the way I would like to spend the next few days, months, years, or however long it takes to arrive at healthy behavior. But I choose to, because the point of Step Seven work is to give up my old ideas and actions to make room for health, love, laughter, and the "sunlight of the Spirit" (*Alcoholics Anonymous*, 4th ed., p. 66).

—*July 2010*

Unclenching My Fist

"Release whatever doesn't bless you." This was part of my meditation this morning, and it struck me that OA has helped me do this by the release of 68 pounds (31 kg) over fifteen months. That release also helped me let go of the pain in my ankles, knees, back, and stomach. That pain was not a blessing!

However, I've been able to release physical weight before. I'm a diet veteran who knows how to read food labels, and I'm a sucker for anything that promises I can "lose 30 pounds (14 kg) in thirty days." I could certainly gorge myself to gain that much, but it never seemed to come off very fast.

What is different this time? The program has allowed me to focus on my emotional and spiritual health and to express and release the sense of hopelessness I felt when I attended my first meetings. I heard, "Focus on working the Steps. That's where you will encounter your Higher Power and receive the gifts of abstinence and right living."

I encountered Step Seven at a Big Book workshop, which gave me the structure to write my Fourth Step inventory, the courage to give it away to my loving sponsor, and the ability to understand and practice right living with the Steps.

But Step Seven—hmmm? I thought I could change my behavior without any real effort. "Lose thirty character defects in thirty days!" That worked the same as the miracle diets—not at all. I believe "release whatever doesn't bless you" is my Higher Power's response to Step Seven. I have humbly asked God to remove my shortcomings and relieve me of my self-centeredness, sense of entitlement, self-righteousness, and fear of not being good enough. I expected they would suddenly be gone forever. That hasn't happened. Until today I was convinced I was doing something wrong.

Instead, I've seen that God is making me more aware of these defects, but not by shining a harsh spotlight on them (that happened when I wrote my inventory). Now God is using a dimmer switch to help me see, for example, when my sense of entitlement makes me angry because things don't go my way. I'm unable to catch it before it happens, but the physical cue of "I need to eat something *now*" causes me to pause and ask, "What's going on here?" I have the opportunity to cease what I am doing or thinking; to make amends, especially to myself; and to not take that first bite.

Today God is telling me to "release whatever doesn't bless me." Step Seven tells us to ask to have our shortcomings removed. God is telling me to unclench my fist and let them go.

—July 2009

Righteous Victimhood

Becoming willing to make amends to people I have harmed is an elusive proposition. To reach the state of willingness, I must first practice forgiveness of self and others.

Unless I can forgive myself for the wrongs I have done to others, I will never overcome the guilt I carry.

To work through the shame, I must look at my act of commission or omission to determine why I did what I did. Assessing my motives may include analyzing the payoff for the bad behavior. In acknowledging the flawed reasons, I better understand my behavior. I can let go of my guilt.

With the clarity that accompanies understanding, I can make amends honestly and sincerely, without a negative, emotional black cloud over my head.

I need to forgive the other person too: Let go of his or her actions toward me, any harm done, and move on. The baggage of righteous victimhood is heavier than the weight of the guilt for the wrongs I've done.

Unless I can forgive others and myself, I will not be making wholehearted amends. Halfhearted amends, like halfhearted measures, avail us nothing.

—August 2004

Amends for Mom

When I was in college, I remember telling a friend, "I wish my mom was dead, so I could collect her life insurance benefit." Although this sounded harsh, it reflected the hurt and anger I felt toward my mom. Fast-forward thirteen years: I talk to my mom often, genuinely tell her "I love you," and help her whenever I can. This is a gift of the program.

When I worked the Steps for the first time, my sponsor helped me to dig deep, see that I had a part in my relationship with my mom, and make amends to her.

Before the program, all I could see were my mom's shortcomings and all the times she had hurt me. After I came to OA, I began to see her with compassion. She was a single parent who struggled to earn a living and raise me. She didn't learn many loving parenting skills from my grandparents, and life had hurt her deeply. If I had been in her shoes, I don't know how much better I would have fared.

My mom's apologies to me were another miracle that healed our relationship. Shortly after I'd made amends to her, she apologized for making many mistakes. She would do things differently and lovingly if she could raise me again. This was an unexpected apology. It helped heal me even more. She still apologizes to me from time to time when we talk about the old days. I tell her, "I know you did your best. I know you had a hard life. Everything is okay now."

This is my miracle story.

—December 2013

How I Made Amends

In September 1981, I came to OA to stay. However, I tried to do it my way for three and a half years. Finally, in February 1985, after becoming sick and tired of being sick and tired, I decided to work the program according to the instructions: to actually do the Steps and to begin to live my life according to them. I have been maintaining my weight of 130 pounds at 5 feet 6 inches (59 kg at 168 cm) for about twenty years by being abstinent and working my program daily.

In the winter and spring of 1985, I did a Step study (and have done several since then). I had been averse to doing Step Four. I thought I would find out something so terrible about myself that I would explode. But I did not!

As to Steps Eight and Nine, I felt I did not have to do them because everyone had done things to me, and I had done nothing to anyone. Right!

Well, my thorough, fearless inventory brought up a lot of stuff for me to face, and I made a list for Step Eight. I became willing, and then I did Step Nine and made amends.

Here are some things I did and how I made amends:

While I was in college, I shoplifted an item from a department store. I never considered that I would not have been able to practice my profession if I had been caught. To make amends for the theft, I sent a money order to the company. They do not prosecute people who send in what they call "conscience money." They are just glad that someone is making restitution. I have not felt the guilt and shame since then, and I do not shoplift today.

I had been in a power play with someone and had treated her badly. She has since died, so I wrote her a letter of amends, put a stamp on it, and mailed it to her in care of heaven. The long-felt guilt lifted. Today I treat people as I would like to be treated: with civility and kindness. I do not always achieve this, but I do keep at it. I hate to apologize, so it is better to keep my mouth closed before putting my size 8 1/2 foot in it!

I made amends to myself by taking care of my health with regular checkups and exercise. I am learning to lighten up and not take life and myself so seriously.

I will never be able to give back to this program what I have been given. I am a happy, grateful compulsive overeater on the road to happy destiny, and I am enjoying the journey.

—*September/October 2009*

Awesome Serenity

My alcoholic parents divorced as soon as I was born. My father wasn't on the scene during my childhood, and my mother couldn't look after my brother, sister, and me. So we lived with our grandmother.

I was an angry child growing up because I didn't have a loving home like other kids at school and felt like the odd one out. Described as an uncontrollable child because of my anger, I had as much fear inside of me as anger.

If I was sitting, my grandmother would say, "If it were your cousin sitting there, she would get a book and read" or "Your cousins are laughing at you because your report card isn't as good as theirs." This caused huge resentments, and I hated her for it. I also blamed her. "If I was taught to be tidy when I was younger, I wouldn't be so messy now," I thought, or "If my grandmother taught me about life, I wouldn't be the way I am now."

When she died, I had so many resentments against her I was glad she was dead. When I commenced my Fifth Step with my sponsor, I told her I couldn't make amends to my grandmother because I had too many strong resentments and they would take a long time to heal. The second time I went through the Steps, I told her the same thing.

I had almost finished my Step Nine amends when suddenly I found myself with pen and paper in hand, writing a letter and making amends. I told my grandmother I was sorry for everything I had ever done to her. I acknowledged she must have been an angry person because she was forced to bring up her daughter's children when she had finished bringing up six of her own. I told her I loved her and thanked her for caring for us. For the first time in my life, I felt the love in my heart for her I had never felt before.

A few days later, I went to her grave and read the letter aloud. Once I had finished making amends and talking to her, I tore up the letter and threw it in a bin. Since then I have felt nothing but love and compassion for my grandmother. I know she forgives me and loves me because I am her granddaughter.

Making amends to my grandmother has given me the freedom to feel at peace within myself and with the world. That peace and serenity are just awesome. No amount of food could ever compensate for that. The love I found for my grandmother still stays with me since that day at the cemetery. I have finally found the freedom to live.

—*September/October 2013*

Self-Forgiveness

In OA, one of my most difficult Steps has been Step Nine, specifically making amends to myself. It has been a challenge to forgive myself for what I falsely believed were terrible mistakes for which I deserved to suffer by eating compulsively and dying slowly in severe pain. I grew up in a religious home that believed in damnation for the unforgiven and nonbelievers. Thanks to my extraordinary physical and emotional sensitivities as an addicted child of addicts, I held on to a set of damaging beliefs throughout my life. My sensitivities magnified the negative messages told to me as a child: I was a sinner, never good enough unless I did what my parents and religion told me to do; I had to be the perfect son to make up for my parents' shortcomings, make straight A's, be the smartest; I was fat, ugly, worthless, and much more.

To disobey my parents was a sin. I hurt them and deserved to be hit with switches and belts when I violated their rules or stirred my father's anger. When I didn't receive physical punishment, my father's emotional withdrawal and silent disapproval were even more painful.

In despair, I joined OA in 1976, carrying the burden of these soul-crushing beliefs. I had early success with weight loss, losing 55 pounds (25 kg) in six months, which I maintain today. I lost the veneer of these false beliefs by working the Steps and living in recovery to the best of my ability. However, I began a long series of ups and downs in OA and serious problems with other addictions that damaged beyond repair my first marriage and a promising career. I felt perplexed because I didn't understand what held me back from long-term abstinence and from receiving the promises of a Twelve Step life.

Thanks to several years of halting recovery through OA, other Twelve Step programs, and long-term therapy, I had a critical revelation. Every time I had worked Steps Four through Nine, especially taking inventory, turning it over, and making amends to others, I had never made amends to myself. I had focused on forgiving others and doing right by them.

I had perpetuated my biggest mistake: blaming myself for everything that had gone wrong. I had never forgiven myself or assigned appropriate responsibility to others. I had no idea what self-forgiveness was or how to do it. I looked up definitions of "forgive" and "forgiveness." They include phrases like "to pardon for a crime or an offense," "to absolve from sin" (I avoided that one like a blazing fire), or "to cancel a debt or liability."

These definitions seemed to be of the "forgive and forget" variety. I know I will always have these memories inside my addict brain. My recovery is a daily reprieve granted by the love and care of my Higher Power. I am not cured, and I have to live in recovery one day at a time. How could I remember and still forgive others and myself?

Fortunately, two other definitions resonate within me. My favorite is to "refrain from imposing punishment." My second favorite is "to stop feeling resentment toward someone else."

To forgive myself means I can stop punishing myself for either the mistakes I've made or the imaginary mistakes I've carried from childhood. I was a child, not a sinner or damaged goods. Children make mistakes because they are imperfect, growing, and learning. I was born a child of God and given the gift of life, not to make up for my parents' deficiencies, but to grow into the person my HP wants me to be. I was punished because of my parents' damaging beliefs.

Not only can I stop punishing myself, I also know my Higher Power loves me and wants me to accept myself for who and what I am: a beloved child of God who has the right to do his best, make mistakes, make amends, and move on to do better. I am not only allowed but encouraged to keep growing as I seek to know and do my HP's will as well as I can, one day at a time.

As I learn to forgive myself, I can also stop resenting my parents, siblings, relatives, and anyone else for what they did to me and for what my hyperactive brain imagines they did to me. I can stop using my memories of the wreckage of my past as an excuse to create the wreckage of my future. I can release the ill will, the belief they owe me anything, and any need to punish them. I can move onward and upward to welcome ever more of my Higher Power's blessings into my life. The promises of freedom, health, happiness, hope, faith, abundance, and joy come true a little more each day, so that I now lead a life in recovery beyond my wildest dreams.

—*December 2013*

4

STEPS TEN TO TWELVE

Reflections on Step Ten

For many years, I've done a written Tenth Step most nights. After experimenting, I've settled on the following system.

I enter the date and thank God for another day of abstinence. Then I focus on the three phases of recovery: physical, emotional, and spiritual. First I address my physical recovery. I review my food choices and exercise program. The main question is: "Did I stay within the boundaries of my plan of eating?" For me, that means three meals a day with nothing in between and no personal binge foods. I commit to correcting any problem areas and plan my meals for the next day.

Then I reflect on my emotional recovery and character defects. Did I practice any of my defects? Do I owe anyone an amends for inappropriate behavior? How might I have reacted to a situation instead of resorting to a character defect? If I owe an amends, I decide how and when I can make it.

Finally, I review my spiritual recovery. Did I turn my will and life over to the care of God, or did I practice self-will in my daily activities? Did I spend time deepening my relationship with my Higher Power through prayer and meditation? I thank God for the favors in my life that day, being specific and citing at least five unique events that I'm grateful for.

This method of doing a Tenth Step is an integral part of my daily program work. It allows me to reflect on the day about to end and identify areas that need further work. I always end the brief writing period feeling clean, ready for a good night's sleep, and prepared for the next day.

—*September/October 2007*

Seeing the Patterns

Since starting to write a regular Tenth Step inventory, I'm becoming aware of two broad patterns. Recognizing this has been a breakthrough for me.

The first is that I am supersensitive. I become hurt easily or angered—justifiably so, I feel. With a daily inventory, I'm beginning to see that sometimes life just doles out harsh blows; hard situations; and rude, self-absorbed, insensitive people. I need to accept this fact and move on, without a heavy emotional investment. Getting unnecessarily bogged down in negative emotions is time-consuming, counterproductive, and deceptive because it prevents me from dealing with emotions generated by genuinely serious events.

The second pattern is that when I respond to a person with an immediate, extreme emotion, that person is often displaying one of my character defects. At first, this realization was most unsettling. Later when I started examining some of my negative emotions toward people, I found even more of my own character defects. Having discovered this, how should I use the information?

Recognizing that I share a defect with another makes it easier to forgive. I try to practice tolerance and understanding. Even if I dislike the other person, I try to be just and courteous. When doing that, I am not judging the other person harshly. Without harsh judgment, I may be open to the prospect of understanding the other person better. In doing that, I understand myself and my character defects better. I may even get to the point where I can treat myself with justice and courtesy. What a concept! With justice, I would treat myself with more honesty and fairness, with an impartial look at my thoughts and actions. With courtesy, I would treat myself with kindness and respect. I don't do any of these things well.

This could be part of my amends to myself, and I could put it into action daily when doing my Tenth Step inventory.

—September/October 2009

Gift of Step Ten

When *Lifeline* asked which Step has had the most impact on my relationship with my family, I wanted to answer "all of them." Countless examples of how the Steps have made my family life happier swirl in my head. Since the question asked me to pick one, Step Ten stands out: Continued to take personal inventory and when we were wrong, promptly admitted it. In fact, Step Ten is good for love and romance.

By the time I met my husband eighteen years ago, I had already worked the Twelve Steps because I had joined OA several years before. But as we got to know each other and decided to spend our lives together, I learned that without my continued work in a Twelve Step recovery program, living with me would be quite a challenge.

Daily action on Step Ten—in written form, as a mental spot-check, or both—cultivates serenity and happiness. Such an inventory clears present anxieties and resentments. It examines the attitudes and actions that allow me to discover selfishness and other character defects. I let go of these defects through prayer: writing to my Higher Power or saying prayers like the Third, Seventh and Eleventh Step Prayers printed in my Tenth Step journal.

When I let go of these resentments, expectations, and fears, "I can watch my serenity level rise" as the Big Book promises (*Alcoholics Anonymous*, 4th ed., p. 420). Step Ten is one of the most romantic actions I can take. It is much easier to love my husband from a position of serenity and acceptance. We are happier as a couple, day by day, because of the Tenth Step. While flowers and a teddy bear are sweet gifts that we give each other on occasion, no gift beats the love of a daily Tenth Step.

—November 2011

Ladders, Not Zappers

How I wish I could have stepped into a machine, turned the dial, and been fixed instantly. Recovery from compulsive eating, sexual abuse, codependency, dysfunctional behaviors, and character defects—gone with a zap! Wouldn't that be great? Unfortunately, life doesn't work that way. Zappers can't fix me. Besides, the zapper machine would probably overload and explode.

I have been on a self-searching journey for many years. I have participated in many self-help and therapy groups and worked with several private counselors. I am grateful for their help on my journey. Each played an important role in my life, aided me in making much-needed changes, and helped me find my way to OA.

God knew it would be too much for me to face my defects all at once, so he had me work on them one step at a time. Some still rear their ugly heads, but thanks to the OA Steps and Tools, I have a way to deal with them when they do. Having this disease is like being stuck in quicksand. OA has provided a ladder to climb out, if I so choose.

Step Ten keeps me safe on shore and away from sinking back into the quicksand daily. I will always have this disease, but I don't have to stay stuck. I am still seeking the miracle of permanent recovery, but I am no longer seeking it in every new diet. Now I am seeking it through my Higher Power and OA and by working my program with my sponsor. Now I can experience freedom. What a gift!

—*September/October 2011*

Marching Orders

S ince I joined OA, I have stopped making New Year's resolutions. By working my program, I've begun to accept myself as I am and life as it is. Trying something new just because the year is increasing by one digit or because we've started a new month or because it's Monday is not a good reason to make a change.

So it surprised me that when last year ended, I was making changes in sync with the calendar. In mid-December, I left my paying job to start a new one—raising my twin girls. I wanted to leave before the holidays so I could focus on my family.

Once I left, my Higher Power started nudging me. First, I restarted my morning writing and have kept it up almost daily. I started exercising, and now I think better and feel stronger. I also began writing down my food consistently. The new thing, though, has been Higher Power's suggestion that I ask in my morning writing for my "marching orders."

What are marching orders? They include a "what" and a "how."

The "what" is asking my Higher Power what Higher Power wants me to do today. As the Big Book says, "We had a new Employer" (*Alcoholics Anonymous*, 4th ed., p. 63). As I worked the Steps, I gave my will and life over to the care of

God (Step Three), so my marching orders are one way of living Step Eleven, "praying only for knowledge of His will for us and the power to carry that out." At work, I knew what my clients' and boss's priorities were and took care of them. Since God is my employer, it's time to do the same with him.

The "how" is simple. I write some version of the question, "Higher Power, what would you have me do today?" I wait for a response and write it down. The result is a to-do list not of my own devising. For example, Higher Power told me to contact my previous employer about health insurance coverage. It turned out a mistake had been made, and I had not received the required paperwork. They rectified the error and reinstated my insurance.

I find that Higher Power's list is usually short, specific, and gentle. Higher Power has been a kinder boss than I ever was. For several days the instruction was to take it easy and rest. I have been told to email certain people, go to the grocery store, make phone calls, and play with the twins.

Sometimes the results of my actions are immediate, such as the health insurance reinstatement, while the outcomes of others have not yet materialized. In the four years I have been in program, I've learned to trust that God will in God's time. For today, I write down my marching orders and execute them to the best of my ability. I trust that Higher Power has the outcome well in hand.

—*November 2008*

100 Meditations, 100 Days

I am working the Steps using *The Twelve-Step Workbook of Overeaters Anonymous*. Every week, I answer questions in the book during my Saturday OA writing meeting. I email my answers to my sponsor throughout the week, which is a great way to reinforce the ideas of recovery.

This month I'm working on Step Eleven. Question ten on page 89 was very helpful. It asks, "What is meditation?" I'd like to share my answer with you.

OA's *Twelve and Twelve* states, "Meditation is an action which gives us much-needed practice in the art of sitting still and opening our hearts to receive spiritual nourishment" (p. 96). That's a good definition. In my own words, I would say meditation is the art of getting still.

Wondrous things occur when I get still. Space opens inside me and Higher Power fills it with life-giving light.

Meditation is the gateway to my true, divine self. When I get quiet long enough, I feel the dross of my ego diminish, and I am left with only God's light.

When I get quiet for only a short amount of time, I store those bits of stillness in my spiritual bank for later use. Every bit of slowing down counts. I must remind myself of this, lest black-and-white thinking take over and I lose my connection to Higher Power.

Some nights my meditation is sixty seconds. I get on my knees, light three candles, set my kitchen timer for one minute, start with a prayer of thanks, and end by asking Higher Power to bless all sentient beings. Other days, it's longer and more formal. On rough days, I make outreach calls and commit to three breaths where I inhale "divine" and exhale "surrender."

Before program, I was irregular in my conscious contact with Higher Power. Most of the time I only connected with

Higher Power when I was in a jam. Because I had little time for peace, my life was tumultuous.

Today, before I get out of bed, I ask Higher Power to walk with me. I say the Third Step Prayer, the Seventh Step Prayer, the Serenity Prayer, and a prayer of thanks for the beautiful day I've been given. It's a great way to align my will with Higher Power's will.

Recently, I committed to meditate one hundred times in one hundred days. I ended up meditating ninety-nine meditations in one hundred days. Failure? Far from it!

I recommit to meditating one hundred times in the next one hundred days. I know more miracles await if I stay connected to my Higher Power.

Thanks for letting me share. For those who are starting out, Step Eleven is something I did from the very beginning. For those who are struggling, HP is waiting for you to reach out. Keep coming back!

—*November 2008*

Daily Conversations with HP

My favorite lines from *The Twelve Steps and Twelve Traditions of Overeaters Anonymous* is "there is no one right way to do step eleven. 'Keep it simple' is a good slogan to apply here. Remembering that our goal is to develop a closer conscious contact with God, prayer is simply what we do when we talk with our Higher Power" (p. 93).

This resonates with me because I am able not only to create my own conception of Higher Power but also to talk with him through what feels like a clear channel. I feel close to him throughout my day and talk to him about everything, but I am careful to never ask for anything other than the knowledge of his will for me.

Upon awakening, I say good morning to my Higher Power while I am still cozy and snuggled in bed. I thank him for my blessings and tell him my plans for the day (meditating is conscious thinking). I ask that my thinking be divorced from self-pity, dishonesty, and self-seeking motives.

Throughout my day, I converse with my Higher Power. A prayer could simply be "thank you for this wonderful gift of an abstinent meal" before I eat, or it could be a discussion of a troublesome situation at work. I might tell my Higher Power about my concerns and reactions and the part I played in things. I pray that I know his will for me.

Before I go to sleep, again snuggled in bed, I thank my Higher Power for the day's blessings and talk to him about how the day went. Next I answer the following questions: Did I pray throughout my day? Was I abstinent? Was I as honest as I could be? Was I kind, gentle, and loving toward all? Am I harboring any resentments? Do I owe an apology or need to make an amends? What fears did I experience, and how did I react to them? What did I do right?

When I talk, my Higher Power listens. When I tell him about my problems, he takes care of them, in his time, in his way. When I ask him to show his will for me, he always does, and my life is richer, fuller, and more joyous. Thank you, Higher Power!

—July 2010

Spirituality, Not Religion

When I first attended OA meetings, the Higher Power thing was a bit disconcerting. Religion was something stuffed down my throat growing up, and I didn't want anything to do with it. I didn't get the difference between religion and spirituality. Step Two was easy for me once I realized it had nothing to do with religion and everything to do with a personal, daily relationship with my creator.

As I read OA literature and the Big Book and heard others in OA talk about their spiritual recovery, I saw more possibilities. At the start, I couldn't believe Higher Power cared what I ate each day. But as my relationship with God deepened, I came to understand that my Higher Power created me and loves me as a mother loves her newborn infant. God cares about every detail of my life.

Early in recovery, I attended a workshop where one of the activities was to write a want ad for God. This opened up the possibilities for me to define my Higher Power. I realized no one knows for certain what God is or isn't, so God can be everything I want and more than I can imagine.

My God is so amazing that I can only conceive of an infinitesimal amount of God's power, goodness, and love. This is the God I want giving me direction, love, and comfort as I work the OA program of recovery. I have been able to let go of my past experiences with religion and trust in my newfound understanding.

God talks to me in so many different ways. Sometimes when I am praying, I get a clear message directing me, especially as I repeat the words, "Thy will be done, not mine." (*For Today,* p. 247). These are powerful words, and I say them often. God also provides direction through other people as I read OA literature or the Big Book, listen to OA Internet speakers, attend OA meetings, or talk to members.

I pray first thing in the morning and last thing before I go to bed. I pray before each meal and throughout the day as I notice those blessings for which I am grateful and thank God. My prayer is either about expressing gratitude or turning it over. I say the Serenity Prayer when I face difficult situations or frustration. When my husband and I have an argument, we often stop, hold hands, and say the Serenity Prayer together. This has been a miracle for our relationship. Prayer opens me up to guidance that is always available, but that I can't always hear.

My life is more peaceful when I am connected to God. I am not alone; I am not in charge. This is so comforting. I don't have to know the answers. I just have to ask for the next right thing and be willing to do it.

—August 2012

Redefining HP

M y definition of Higher Power has changed in a dramatic way over the seven years I have been in program.

I joined OA when I was 23, with a strong belief in the God of my religion. He was my Higher Power, and he worked for me. He was a gentle, loving, fatherly figure who watched over me and had a hand in everything that happened to me. I trusted him, and I believed he had my best interests in mind and would lead me to great happiness. I was comfortable with this idea and relied on this Higher Power for several years. He sounds pretty nice, doesn't he?

The only problem was this idea wasn't a product of my own discovery. I was taught about God from birth and educated in religious schools. My husband and most of my friends were of the same religion. I believed it because I was told it was true, not because it made sense to me. I am not disparaging my first notion of Higher Power. It worked; I got abstinent and made much progress in recovery. However, it was a childish state, and the time came to grow up.

A couple of years ago, my husband began a serious questioning of our faith. I was not interested at first. I was quite happy with things as they were. It was a gradual process, but I became willing to open my mind to new ideas. My questioning began. I read books; talked with many people; and with a critical eye, examined my beliefs. They weren't based on much more than tradition and what people told me was true. The beliefs did not make sense to me.

I would not have been able to do this exploration earlier in recovery. I didn't know myself well enough to know what I thought. I needed people to tell me what to do and what to believe.

It was the same with my program. At first I needed a sponsor to tell me how to work the Steps and Tools, give me assignments, and be involved with my food plan. Taking direction served me at that stage of recovery. As with my religion, the time came to take more responsibility for my program and to do what works. I learned I am motivated by the desire for approval as a good girl. Doing things my own way is hard but good.

The questioning process was scary, as all change is for me. I was afraid to let go of God as I understood him. Would I lose my recovery? Would I want to leave OA? What would my family think? Those were a few of my many fears, but I held on to the Principles of OA. I was open with my sponsor and other trusted friends. When my husband and I decided to leave our religion, we were also open with our families. We got many questions and some disappointment, but the ultimate result was acceptance and support.

I no longer believe in the "big guy in the sky," nor is anything the ultimate authority. I believe in inner goodness and brotherly love and in respecting everyone and everything because they are here. I have great respect for nature and the life process. I find "GOD" in the Good Orderly Direction I receive working a Twelve Step program. Most important, I have an open mind and a humble heart (on good days). I am okay with saying, "I don't know."

I feel great about the changes I've experienced through this process. I know myself better and love the person I am finding. I am more honest and accepting and less judgmental and fearful. I'm thrilled the journey will continue. This is an amazing, exciting life. I feel privileged to be here, abstinent and able to experience it. Peace to you all.

—August 2012

Source of Kindness

"What wisdom can you find that is greater than kindness?" I have been thinking about how this Jean Jacques Rousseau quote (*For Today*, p. 344) applies to the three parts of Step Twelve.

A big part of the spiritual awakening I have had through working my OA program is an awareness of the power of kindness. One of my coping ways has been to acquire knowledge, to try to become a source of wisdom. I have attained some wisdom, but not what I expected. I do have education and recognized credentials and acknowledge their value. In OA I have learned that being kind, meeting people where they are, listening without judgment, and trusting in an individual's personal process are true wisdom. Each person I meet has a Higher Power, and it is not I. Kindness is a more powerful service than advice.

Kindness is the better way to carry the message of recovery. I believe the love and acceptance I felt as a newcomer opened my mind and heart to the program of Overeaters Anonymous and to much more of life than I had experienced. I learned to respect and value the wisdom of other people in the rooms. What keeps me coming back year after year is the kindness of members who allow me to be myself, working my way through the Steps without having others tell me what I should do.

Practicing these Principles in all our affairs is a practical application of kindness in daily life. Many years ago, my 2-year-old, newly adopted son woke me in the middle of the night with his crying. I picked him up and rocked him, angry and resentful at the interruption of my sleep. I was fuming silently, and he was shrieking. When I remembered to pray the Serenity Prayer, I also began to wonder what it must be like for that little boy to be awake and afraid in a strange place. As soon as I shifted my attention from my discomfort to his feelings, he stopped crying and fell asleep. My willingness to be kind was far more valuable in that instance than any of the childcare books I might have consulted.

In OA I have also heard, "Would you rather be happy or right?" I used to imagine that always being right would make me happy. I now prefer to be happy and a source of kindness rather than a font of information.

I am very grateful to be a member of OA and to often witness both true and genuine kindness.

—December 2013

Steps to Integrity

L iving the Twelve Steps of Overeaters Anonymous has changed my life for the better. By admitting my powerlessness over food, I can see how trying to control it was making my life unmanageable. OA has guided me in developing a belief in a Higher Power that works for me. This restores me to sanity and brings me peace. Developing a relationship with God allows me to turn my will and my life over to his care daily.

By making a searching and fearless moral inventory of myself, I see my character defects and assets clearly.

Admitting the exact nature of my wrongs to God, my sponsor, and myself forces me to discuss why I did the thing I did. It also helps me understand that not everything was my fault, and I am able to release much of the guilt and shame that caused me to overeat.

Understanding my old ways of coping—overeating, lying, cheating, stealing—opens my mind to using the Tools of the program. I am willing to allow God to remove my character defects because now I don't need them to survive.

I've heard that if I'm not willing to do something, I should pray for the willingness to be willing. As I become more willing to let go of my character defects, I become more willing to ask God to remove them.

Having made a list of people I had harmed, I have become willing, one day at a time, to make amends to all of them, and I have made amends to some of them. My sponsor helps me decide when making an amends would injure that person or someone else, and then I write my amends and put it in my God box.

I take a daily personal inventory. Sometimes I do this in a letter to God, in prayer at the end of the day, or in a conversation with my husband, sponsor, or OA friend. I try to promptly admit when I'm wrong, but I still struggle with pride and ego. When this happens, I remember progress, not perfection.

I pray often. In troubling times, I pray to HP instead of running to the food. I am working on my relationship with God, which means I have to communicate with him regularly. I treat our relationship like I would any other important friendship.

Meditation is something I must work at. I've tried formal ways of meditating, but I fall asleep. I have learned that prayer is my way of talking with God, and meditation is God's way of talking with me. If I remember this, I find that I meditate throughout the day. That feeling of my conscience speaking to me is my Higher Power speaking to me. If I listen, I am better for it. His will, not mine, be done.

Carrying the message to other compulsive overeaters is my favorite part of the program. I love sharing the experience, strength, and hope I've found in OA. I am committed to practicing the OA Principles in all my affairs. I find that when I do, I feel good about myself and live with integrity. It doesn't matter if I'm treated fairly; HP will take care of me. It does matter if I've treated others fairly.

—*September/October 2006*

5

TOOLS OF RECOVERY

Hidden Part

I want to eat. I reach for the food, but what am I really reaching for? I am not hungry—not for food. I'm hungry for comfort, warmth, and inner calm. I'm hungry to be loved and have fun. I search for what to do, how to handle my issues and situation—and I reach for the food.

But I stop myself. I write this instead. Writing—what a helpful Tool! I keep my hands busy and my mind focused on the task before me. I forget the food while my Higher Power provides answers through my writing. Is that the hidden part of the Tools I'd never seen? They can rescue me right now.

I knew the Tools were central to the program and my recovery in a big picture kind of way, but now I see how they can also rescue my sanity and recovery in a moment of need. I call someone, and I don't eat while dialing or talking. I focus on the conversation and get out of my head. I write my thoughts and release the feelings, focusing on my writing and occupying my hands. I do service in any form, which reminds me about the program. Sometimes when I'm with another OA person and doing a good deed, I feel good about myself. So, how could I eat!

I go to a meeting—no food allowed! I talk to my sponsor, who tells me what I need to hear, and the food goes away without me even realizing it.

I read the literature, occupying my hands and mind, focusing on the words of hope and courage. How could I break my abstinence while reading the Big Book, the OA *Twelve and Twelve,* or *Lifeline*?

I follow my written food plan; it frees me from thinking about what I'll eat. Doing so allows me to focus on more productive things, like my recovery and life. I remember what it was like before my abstinence, and I do whatever it takes to keep this beautiful gift my Higher Power has provided. I cherish my abstinence.

So use the Tools, whichever you wish and whichever works best for you at that moment. The Tools are key to our recovery over time, but they also help keep us abstinent in the moment. The Tools are always available. So reach for the Tools instead of the food. They are always ready to come to the rescue.

—March/April 2012

Free to Change!

I came to OA in 1993, weighing in excess of 250 pounds (113 kg). No *Dignity of Choice* pamphlet existed. In fact, talking about food was taboo and rumors abounded of colored sheets available in the back alley after the meeting. I wondered if the food police would pop out of nowhere if a newcomer mentioned the round thing with a hole in the center!

At my first meeting, it became clear I needed a sponsor and food plan. I wanted to be abstinent, though I was not clear what that meant. My sponsor suggested I call her the next day with my plan for the day and not eat sugar. It was that simple.

My first food plan was calorie counting more or less. With time, I recognized the need to abstain from certain foods. My plan has evolved as needed. It began as a weight-loss tool, but it became a maintenance tool when I reached a goal weight.

In my eighteen years of recovery, I have increased or decreased food to compensate for health issues, exercise, and aging. Doggone it; I don't need as much food today!

Weighing my food helps me know I am eating the right amount for my physical recovery. I plan the evening before, write it down, and report it to my sponsor. Then I don't have to worry about food, leaving much more time to live my life.

The most important thing I can share with a newcomer is that a food plan is just a tool that helps me gain, lose, or maintain weight. Like any tool, if it's not working, I can fix it (with my sponsor's help) or get a new one. I'm not married to my food plan until death do us part. As my life has evolved, so has the quantity I eat. My abstinence is not my food plan, but having a good food plan helps me stay abstinent.

—May 2011

Power of Meetings

For the first twenty-nine years of my life, I never spoke to anyone about my secret binges and food rituals. I didn't say anything about the mind torture I experienced after the first bite was gone; the expected bliss evaded me, and I kept eating anyway. I had never revealed to anyone that I would eat an entire pizza and then do two hours of aerobics and take laxatives to get rid of it. And I had never heard anyone else discuss these things.

I thought I was the only one. I thought other overweight people had thyroid problems or health issues that kept them fat. I thought other people who exercised a lot were just being extra healthy.

Then something amazing happened. In August 1999, I attended my first meeting of Overeaters Anonymous. I listened to a tall, thin, healthy-looking woman share her story of experience, strength, and hope. She said she had done things with food that were very similar to the things I had done. She shared the anxiety and fear she felt because of her inability to stop eating, even when she knew she was harming herself.

When the picture book she passed around the meeting room got to me, I saw what she used to look like: an overweight, unhappy, and unhealthy woman.

I heard and saw myself in this woman. I watched as other people in the room nodded their heads as she talked. Had they done the same things and experienced the same feelings? I couldn't believe they were sharing the truth openly, with no shame.

That first OA meeting has stayed with me for thirteen years. It has been the foundation of my program of recovery, showing me that face-to-face meetings are a vital part of my personal growth. When I am sitting in a meeting; listening to others share; seeing them nod their heads when I share; and exchanging hugs, smiles, and tears before and after the meeting, I remember some important facts.

First, I remember I am not unique in my disease. I am not the only person who has suffered from the consequences of compulsive overeating. I am not the only person who has had to face the fact that I am powerless over food. I am not the only person who has lost weight and been left with stretch marks and hanging skin that make that wished-for bikini body a castle in the sky.

Second, I remember I don't have to face this disease alone. When I need help, all I have to do is go to a meeting or pick up the phone and call another recovering compulsive overeater.

Third, I remember my Higher Power wants me to listen to and help others. In meetings, I find that sharing my experience, strength, and hope has been helpful to others, just as that woman's story was helpful to me at my first meeting. A friend in program often refers to others in the program as "God with skin on" because she inevitably hears the message God wants her to hear when she goes to a meeting. It might be difficult to hear the message, If I don't work through the Twelve Steps and live by their Principles, I will go back to compulsive overeating. Many times I have heard people coming back from relapse share that exact message. Their willingness to share the horrors of relapse has saved me time and time again from picking up that first compulsive bite when I thought I just couldn't do it anymore.

Finally, as I celebrate my thirteenth year of abstinence, I am overwhelmed with gratitude for the Tool of meetings. When I think about the meetings I've attended, I see the faces of people who have helped me carry on for one more day. I hear the words of others, who are sometimes struggling or sometimes thriving, who have inspired me to stay clean through tumultuous as well as peaceful times. I feel the strength their sharing has given me when I face the breakroom at work, filled with sugary goodies, and put my weighed-and-measured lunch in the microwave. And I remember their perseverance when I don't feel like getting up early to do my Step work and morning meditations before beginning my day.

Together we can!

—*February 2013*

No Brighter

Frequent contact with newcomers is the bright spot of my life. I don't know how it works, but it does. In fact, I had an encounter with a newcomer that was miraculous.

As I drove my daughter to the airport one morning, the food was calling. I had had my abstinent breakfast, but as I drove down the freeway I checked out the food-joint signs at each exit. At the airport, other people probably saw airplanes, gates, and waiting areas. Not me—I could only focus on the food outlets.

As I left the airport, I felt that if I did not stuff my face with food in the next five minutes, I would die. But as I approached each exit, I was sure the perfect binge was a little farther down the road. At one point, as my knuckles were white on the steering wheel, I remembered my Higher Power has a part in all of this. I prayed for God's help. I knew about a noon OA meeting I could get to if God would take over and get me there. God did. I was late, but made it. I had hoped that just walking through the door would make me feel better, but it didn't. I didn't share and didn't listen to anything that was shared. All I could think about was where I was going to binge as soon as the meeting was over.

As we stood hand in hand saying the Serenity Prayer, I prayed it would be over soon so I could go. Finally we got to "it works if you work it." I turned to grab my purse and run, just as the woman next to me turned to me and said, "I'm new; could you answer a few questions for me?" The food stopped calling—instantly! I had a wonderful conversation with her, introduced her to other folks, exchanged phone numbers, and did all the good things we do with newcomers in this Fellowship.

Did I help her that day? Perhaps. I hope so.

Did she help me that day? No. She saved my life. Talk about a bright spot! I don't think they get any brighter!

—*January 2008*

Hearing, Seeing Commonalities

I am an OA member who is hard of hearing. I believe my perspective has enriched the lives of others in the program. I don't know how many of them have met a hard-of-hearing person before they met me. I used to think my disability made me different from others in OA and they wouldn't understand where I was coming from. Boy, did I ever find out I was wrong!

I believe we, as compulsive overeaters, have more in common with one another than we have differences. We have a shared perspective and similar way of looking at the world, particularly if we are in recovery. We understand the pain of being enslaved to food on physical, emotional, and spiritual levels. We can identify with each other's feelings. One doesn't need to be hard of hearing or deaf to know the feelings of sadness, anger, and loss. We all have experienced them to varying degrees. More important, as we grow in our recovery, we learn what OA can do for us, and what we can do for the greater good of OA.

We understand that recovery lies in using the Tools of the program, working the Steps, and helping each other. I can't write this article without discussing the telephone as one of the recovery Tools. I struggle with using this Tool, not only because of my inability to hear. I struggle for the same reasons others in OA do. It comes back to my fear of reaching out to others in program.

Thoughts such as these run through my head: "Will I be bothering them?" "What will they think of me, picking up the phone and admitting to a weak moment?" "What will they think when I ask them to repeat something on the phone?" My old fears of self and "ego run riot" surface, and I have to realize the phone is a Tool like any other in program. It's there for people to use, as needed; to reach out and not isolate; and to stay or get into recovery, as the case may be.

I feel more connected to my friends in program, my recovery, and my Higher Power when I use the phone. I also supplement the phone Tool with email. My deafness is no impediment to using email during the week to stay in touch with others in my meeting. And sometimes in email, we can go deeper and share more than is possible in the three minutes my meeting allots for sharing. I have sent my food choices to others via email and have found this keeps me accountable for what I am eating.

As a hard-of-hearing person, I have more in common with other compulsive overeaters than not. I try to remember this when the differences rise to the surface. I also know my Higher Power looks beyond the differences in people to see and acknowledge the ways in which we are similar.

—February 2008

Stargazing

Have you ever had one of those days when everything goes wrong? I had one recently. It happened to fall on the day of an OA meeting. I was so depressed by the end of the day I thought, "Oh, I just won't go to my meeting. Something bad will probably happen there too, like nobody will come but me!"

So I called two of my OA friends and asked if they could come early to the meeting to talk about this, so I could get over it. They both had other plans. They were coming to the meeting but couldn't come early. Great!

I ate an abstinent meal—a miracle of God after the day I had had—and went to the meeting place early. I decided to write about my day. A good Step One was in order, but I had so many bad things happen that I didn't know where to start!

I made a list of everything that had happened and ended up with ten things. I was so down in the dumps, I decided to look at the negative aspects of each event and, for recovery, write the positive aspects. For instance, my dad was dying. I wrote that it was difficult to watch someone slowly die and not be able to do anything for him. I felt helpless and sometimes hopeless. Death is not easy to accept, especially when it is slow and painful for a loved one. I hate it.

Then I wrote down the positives of my dad dying. Yes, there were some positives! I discovered I had been given this opportunity to get to know my dad. I was always afraid of him when I was growing up. He was verbally abusive to the family, and we were afraid of his temper. I never knew until the past couple of years that my dad has a wonderful sense of humor!

I had been enjoying his sense of humor and how he had been handling death. I had also been getting close to my dad because I had made my amends to him years ago and had no anger toward him. I could see him as he really was: a sick old man. I loved him.

Death brought the opportunity to say, "I love you"! It was never said much in our house, just always understood. To hell with that! I had been telling my dad all along I loved him. Just recently he had started saying, "I love you too"! Wow! I had been waiting my whole life to hear those words. Death made that possible.

So I went through my list of bad things like that, listing the negatives and the positives. Amazingly, the positives far outweighed the negatives. Imagine that! I finished writing and took a nap. I needed some rest. I felt better.

We had ten people at our OA meeting that night, three of them newcomers. (We normally have about four people.) Wow! Was that a blessing or what? We were working on Step

Twelve, part of which basically says, If you want to get out of yourself, start working with another compulsive eater. I heard you, God!

It was a great meeting, and I felt like I was walking on air! I went home, and my niece who was visiting from out of town was there. When I stepped in the door, I mentioned what a gorgeous night it was outside with so many visible stars. My husband, niece, and I decided to stargaze. We found the Big Dipper first and went on from there. How could I feel bad when such beauty surrounded me? My bad day was just a small part of the universe—real, but tiny.

I ended up spending the evening with people I love and having a good time. What changed? My attitude! I was no longer negative, so my day was better. I felt better, had an attitude of gratitude, and started counting my blessings instead of hanging onto the negative part of my day. I felt good because I focused on my recovery instead of my disease.

I am well and have so much to be grateful for! Thank you, God!

—December 2006

Sanity Tools

I joined OA five months ago, and my life has never been better. My compulsive overeating started about forty years ago, getting progressively worse at the conclusion of each diet. I was able to lose weight, but as soon as I lost control I would gain back all the weight and then some. Each time, I sank deeper into myself, shutting family and friends out of my life. I had promised myself I would get my weight and life under control by the time I turned 50, but with only four months until my fiftieth birthday, I was running out of time. I had tried every diet out there, and none had worked. I thought my only hope was to have my stomach stapled. My husband was not happy with the idea, but I was desperate.

While reading the newspaper, I saw a small article about OA meetings in our area. I called, got directions, and three days later went to my first meeting. Although I was very nervous, I knew I belonged, and a feeling of peace came over me. I became abstinent two days later, and I'm maintaining my abstinence. I don't know how much weight I've lost because part of my abstinence is staying off the scales, but I've dropped four sizes and am grateful for this.

My journey hasn't been easy, and sometimes it has been hour by hour. Every day since my first day, I have used all the Tools available to me, and I attend two OA meetings a week. I start my day with the Serenity Prayer, read passages from *For Today* and *Voices of Recovery*, and say a prayer for protection. Each day, I seek help from my Higher Power for guidance on my meals and anything that comes up during the day, and I end the day writing in my journal about what happened. I spend thirty minutes to an hour reading OA literature.

Some days I don't feel like reading, but I tell myself this could be the disease trying to creep back into my life. I just can't leave anything out of my new routine because my sanity depends on it. I love my new life; food no longer rules it. Gone are the days of running to the store to buy food to replace what I binged on at home. No more hiding in the house with the drapes drawn.

I will forever be grateful to OA. I have my life back, and my relationships with my husband, family, and friends have greatly improved. OA has brought God back into my life, and my new OA family has helped me more then they will ever know.

—*May 2006*

Savoring a Cool Lifeline

Even after joining OA, I have been tempted to eat compulsively, but *Lifeline* has been there for me. Instead of reaching for something in the refrigerator, I reach for a *Lifeline*. OA members, like me, write the stories, so the articles are from the heart.

People laugh when I share what I started doing years ago when feeling the urge to eat compulsively: I wanted to do anything to stay abstinent, so in addition to calling my sponsor and OA friends, praying to my Higher Power, and committing to my spouse I would not eat until mealtime, I put a couple of *Lifeline*s in the refrigerator!

When my compulsive side wants to flirt with what's inside the fridge, the presence of these *Lifeline*s stops my compulsion cold. I laugh as I take out a nice, cool *Lifeline* and savor every chilly article instead of a chilly, not-on-my-food-plan food.

I have had the privilege of membership in OA since January 1990 and have subscribed to *Lifeline* since then. *Lifeline*, in conjunction with the Tools, Steps, and Traditions, gives me an amazing life and keeps me at least 75 pounds (34 kg) from my heaviest weight. I hope OA members will make room in their mailboxes and refrigerators for *Lifeline*. The program works when I work it—any way I can!

—February 2006

Action Plan

At OA's 2011 World Service Business Conference, delegates voted on the definition of action plan. It included much more than movement. I now realize I have been following an action plan since I started program! My first actions were getting a sponsor and food plan, then becoming willing to take direction and work the Steps.

My action plan has evolved over the years. I have worked on balancing work and family; dealt with financial insecurity; organized my home; and taken care of medical, dental, and vision issues. I have incorporated meditation into my daily routine, and prayer is essential for remembering who is in charge: God, not me.

I am maintaining a 210-pound (95-kg) weight loss, but as I age (I am 65 and a half), my weight has fluctuated. I have two choices: to refine my food plan or to exercise. That dreaded "e" word has found me again. My choice today is to exercise. I walk every day for twenty-five minutes at a safe-but-challenging pace. I stretch and lift weights three times a week. I am also starting yoga.

My action plan may change as life changes. As long as my focus is on physical, spiritual, and emotional recovery, my actions will align with my Higher Power. God gave me this life as a gift; I want to return it with appreciation.

—January 2012

Say Yes to Action

Two years ago, I was thrilled by the feeling of a pair of size 8 pants fitting! I also remember the thrill of putting on summer clothes on the first warm day of the year and finding they fit. For the past two or three years, my body size has been pretty stable.

How do I keep my program fresh?

Remembering the nature of the illness of compulsive overeating

Every now and then, I am reminded of the liveliness and creativity of my illness. At Halloween I wanted to eat the kids' candy. I thought, "If I didn't have the program, I would want to nick some of their candy." I do not often walk around thinking about candy and sugar, so I was in the danger zone. I discussed this with an OA member, wrote about it, and admitted I am still as powerless over food as I was seven years ago when I first came to program.

Working with my sponsees

A few months ago, one of my sponsees was having difficulties staying abstinent. She was bingeing, so I proposed she call me every day over lunch. I have never called my sponsor every day, so my sponsee and I did not know what the result would be or how it would work. But as my sponsee began calling me every day, I realized having a daily talk on a sponsor-sponsee basis felt good. Now I am quicker to pick up the phone and call my own sponsor!

Participating in program activities

I participate in program activities beyond my meetings, including special workshops, retreats, holiday celebrations, and get-togethers. These activities allow me to meet people from other meetings and other anonymous programs. It is stimulating to discuss the Steps and Traditions with them and to feel connected through these Twelve Steps, no matter what the addiction.

To keep my program fresh, all I need to do is take what's there in the moment and say "yes." I don't need to search for cravings, be responsible for my sponsees' binges, or organize every program event myself. As opportunities arise, I deal with or embrace them. OA is and will remain a program of action. I hope compulsive eaters will say yes to the actions the program proposes and find relief from compulsive eating too.

—*May 2010*

Perspectives on Anonymity

The Principle of anonymity, as embodied in the Eleventh and Twelfth Traditions, is at the heart of our program. In AA's *Twelve Steps and Twelve Traditions,* Bill Wilson says that "humility, expressed by anonymity, is the greatest safeguard that Alcoholics Anonymous can ever have," (page 187) and yet anonymity continues to be the least understood Principle within the Fellowship.

What does anonymity mean? We all know we should not reveal our own membership at the public level or reveal other people's membership without their permission. But much more than that caused the cofounder of Alcoholics Anonymous to think it of such importance, and several publications are available to help us learn more about it.

The OA and AA *Twelve Steps and Twelve Traditions* books are the primary sources of understanding for many of us. We also have several pamphlets that discuss Traditions Eleven and Twelve and their practical application: *The Twelve Traditions of Overeaters Anonymous*; *The Tools of Recovery*; and *OA Handbook for Members, Groups, and Intergroups*. Numerous audio recordings, especially those from World Service Business Conferences, are also useful.

Perhaps the best pamphlet on the subject is *Anonymity: The Meaning and Applications of Traditions Eleven and Twelve*. This little pamphlet, available from OA's online bookstore (bookstore.oa.org), is a collection of four articles written by our founder, Rozanne S. The first article, "The Promise of Privacy," discusses anonymity from the perspective of a newcomer to our Fellowship. It covers the newcomer's fear and shame, the promise that the newcomer need not reveal his or her membership to anyone until ready, and the assurance that we can share in meetings and know that our words will not be repeated.

The second article, "The Initial Confusion," tells us that the anonymity Tradition was born of fear, but has come to mean much more. It explains that revealing our full names at levels other than "press, radio, films, television, and other public media of communication" is within the Traditions and that the choice to do so is ours as individuals. Telling friends, neighbors, health professionals, and coworkers about our membership helps carry the message to those who may need our help one day. On a more practical level, many of us have discovered that last names are useful when we want to visit a sick member in the hospital, send a postcard to an OA friend, or receive mail from our region or the World Service Office.

"In the Public Media," the third article, explains the reasons for maintaining anonymity, both one's full name and face, at the level of the media. The anonymity Principle protects us from our egos and our desire, perhaps, for fame or financial reward. It also protects OA from damage that could be done by a person known to be a member who returned to the food. As individuals, we can talk about OA without mentioning our membership, but at the public level we never reveal our membership and give identifying details. Because the media may not know about our anonymity Principle or consider it important, it is up to us to clarify this point. Most media contacts are happy to comply when they know the reason.

The final article, "Our Spiritual Foundation," gets to the heart of anonymity. It states, "To be anonymous in OA means to be one among many, to accept ourselves as no better or worse than our fellows" (p. 8). True humility stems from this position. When we finally realize we are not special, different, a nonentity, or superior to others, we learn the true nature of our disease and discover a base for a life of "sane and happy usefulness" (*Alcoholics Anonymous,* 4th ed., p. 130) in recovery from compulsive overeating. Within OA, none of us is a star or a VIP. We serve in different ways, and no service position gives any of us authority over others. Anonymity is a reminder that it is the message, not the messenger, that will help another suffering compulsive overeater and that the credit for our recovery goes to God, not to ourselves.

—February 2005

6

Carrying the Message through the Tools of Service and Sponsorship

Never Ending Journey

S ervice is the spiritual Principle of Step Twelve. Doing Twelfth Step work is one of my greatest joys in program today. When I can do service, stop being centered on self, and get into the solution with a fellow compulsive overeater, I am brought closer to the God of my understanding.

I know that in my first two to three years of recovery, I had the notion that I could one day leave the rooms because I would have arrived at the end of my OA journey. I know today that I have not and I will not. This is a continuous journey, one day at a time, for the rest of my life. It says on page 100 of the OA *Twelve and Twelve* that we never arrive, "even when we've reached a goal of health, body size, or weight; even when we've worked all twelve steps to the best of our ability; even when we've celebrated milestone anniversaries of abstinence and recovery; even when we've been placed in positions of trust by other OAs and have rendered service on the group, inter-group, regional, and international levels."

This tells me my service journey is never ending. The same goes for my OA program journey. I will not graduate from OA service or OA program. Overeaters Anonymous teaches me I will only continue my spiritual growth as long as I work the Twelve Steps. I must do this work everyday. I cannot rest and relax in the results of the work I did yesterday. I cannot be complacent with what I have already received through service work and not make any further efforts. I do not have the luxury of resting on my laurels. Also on page 100, it says we need to "keep developing our spiritual consciousness, if we are to remain spiritually awake and spiritually alive" (*The Twelve Steps and Twelve Traditions of Overeaters Anonymous*).

My life is, indeed, much more happy, joyous, and free to-day. My spiritual life is much more alive. I am in a beautiful, loving, nurturing relationship with God, as I understand God. That's because of the work I have done and will continue to do in this God-blessed and God-inspired program of Overeaters Anonymous!

I write this with sincere gratitude for the honor to be of service and to continue my spiritual growth through this writing.

—June 2013

Willing and Able

I had returned from a region assembly and was reflecting on my gratitude for the experience. I thought of my journey into service.

The only prerequisite for OA service is to be willing and able. At first I did not know if I wanted to do service, but I had the willingness to investigate intergroup. I had three questions about intergroup. To get answers, I decided to attend as a visitor.

First, I wanted to know if intergroup attendees handled the meeting well. Yes, the meeting began and ended on time and followed an agenda. Everyone had a voice and a vote.

Second, I wondered if I would feel welcome. I did. The meeting members invited me to choose a committee to sit in on, and I felt included there.

Finally, I wanted to know what the intergroup representatives did and if I could handle the position. I saw an open environment that allowed representatives do what they could take on. More experienced representatives led the way.

From the seed of willingness, I became ready to make a three month commitment to be a voting intergroup representative. In the seven years since, I've served three terms as an intergroup committee chair on two different committees. I spent two years on the intergroup board as treasurer, learning many new skills. Now, I have begun my first term as intergroup chair.

I am beginning my third term as a region representative after having rotated out of that position after two terms. In my first term as region representative, I served one year as a committee chair and am serving this term as a committee vice-chair.

I served two terms as a World Service Business Conference delegate. In that position, I was fortunate to spend all four years on the same committee, including one year as a subcommittee chair, one year as vice-chair, and my final year as delegate cochair.

Service in OA has kept me growing both spiritually and emotionally. It's inspired me to learn more and more about our amazing Twelve Traditions and Twelve Concepts, which grease the service wheels to move OA forward in our mission of reaching out to still-suffering compulsive eaters.

Sometimes service has kept me from behaving compulsively with food because I would choose giving abstinent service over food. Most of all, OA service beyond the group level has allowed me the privilege to meet and know so many inspiring, trusted servants who really walk the walk and have imparted, along with their experience and strength, the hope that gives me the strength to remain recovered and walking with them, one day at a time.

—*December 2013*

Inspiring Intergroup

I became an intergroup representative about nine months ago. It was a six month commitment. My job was to show up, take notes, grab flyers, and report back to my meeting. I figured I could handle that. New things are often scary for me, so it's important I take things slowly.

I didn't know what to expect at my first intergroup meeting. I found familiar faces from my meetings and faces new to me, though not new to OA. I loved joining hands and saying the Serenity Prayer before getting down to business. It calmed my nerves because it reminded me HP was with us. I was grateful for a place where I could say, "I'd like to consider that task. Let me take a few weeks to check with my sponsor and Higher Power."

The support I found through intergroup was fluid and vibrant. I learned how others work with diligence to balance service in their lives. I saw how kindness, respect, and even humor help us to handle disagreements. I learned interpersonal skills just by watching others let go and let God. What a gift!

Once my term ended, I wanted to continue as part of my lively, committed intergroup. A number of committees needed a chair, so I prayed for a month and asked my sponsor for feedback. After my prayer time, I volunteered to chair the Newcomers Committee because it was new and had no existing task list.

Learning to set healthy, manageable goals, delegate responsibilities to other willing members, and surrender my will to my Higher Power are perfect ways to practice balancing service and life. HP shows me what needs to be done and what can wait. When the time comes, I will humbly pass the torch to another member who is open to chairing this committee.

Each time I give service, my HP is shining through me. Every effort of loving service makes a difference. You can share your love too! It's as easy as showing up to an intergroup meeting and asking which committees need help. You don't have to jump right in. My favorite new phrase is, "I'll pray on it and get back to you."

—June 2012

Inner Workings

I do intergroup service for several reasons. First, my home group did not have an active intergroup representative when I first came to OA. The group asked for a volunteer, and no hands went up, so I volunteered. In my professional life, I am always the one asking for volunteers. Volunteers are indispensable in organizations trying to do worthwhile things. So with very little experience in OA but knowing that volunteering lubricates the world's soul, I agreed.

Another reason I serve as an intergroup representative is so I can learn OA's big picture. Working with like-minded people from other groups who love to serve and are struggling to recover from compulsive overeating, I have learned more about the actual structure of OA than I ever would have by simply reading or picking up bits and pieces of information in my home group.

I want to help my home group make a big contribution, not only to our own members but also to those who still suffer in and out of our rooms. As I learn how it all fits together, I can motivate others and reach beyond our walls.

Finally, I know those who serve grow spiritually and emotionally in an exponential way because I believe that is how my

Higher Power designed the inner workings of the universe. I want as much recovery and abstinence as time will allow, and serving others through my home group and intergroup makes it likely my desire to help other sufferers will be successful!

—July 2014

Region Reps Rock!

I n fall 2011, I took God's gentle urging to become more involved in my intergroup's activities. In the past I shied away from intergroup service because I didn't want to be accountable to a group or risk not doing something well.

Miracle of miracles, I saw an ad in our intergroup newsletter for the position of region representative. (OA has ten regions worldwide.) I asked others in the Fellowship what a region representative did. I learned the duties included attending region assemblies, which take place twice a year; bringing our intergroup's concerns to region board members/region reps; voting according to my beliefs regarding the best interests of our area's members; and bringing back information from the region to intergroups and individual meetings.

I thought I could perform these duties without too much effort or time. As a working mom of twins, I must consider many things before accepting obligations. I attended the next intergroup meeting, and to my surprise, I received a unanimous vote.

I attended my first assembly in October 2011. It was scary because I had no clue what was going on. But more than that, it was amazing! I met so many new fellows with whom I still text, email, or call. The region takes good care of their new representatives. The board hosts a new-representative orientation, and each new rep has a mentor to answer questions and assist with the process. The assembly voted on the nuts and bolts of OA work with respect to spreading our message.

Most important, our board members showed inspiring recovery. Each member had attained or was working toward a healthy body weight. I felt so much hope when I saw the board members meeting the strict criteria required and giving of themselves for the good of our Fellowship.

After the assembly, I wondered if it would be possible to attain a healthy body weight and achieve complete freedom from food obsession. The next week I got honest with HP about my eating and asked for the willingness to remove foods from my plan that were hampering my weight loss. From that weekend to now, I have lost 47 pounds (21 kg). For the first time in my adult life, I wear single-digit-sized clothes and have achieved a healthy body weight. The compulsion to eat has been removed for today. If I had not stepped out in faith with my HP and seen other fellows who exemplified recovery, I might still be abstinent from sugar and binge foods but not free from the compulsion.

I am now chair of a region committee, another job I tried to get out of because I did not think I could handle it. But HP has equipped me with all I need to accomplish the duties of the office. Service keeps me from isolating and gives me opportunities to share what has been freely given to me. It has helped me develop new skills, such as public speaking and organizing committee work. Thank you, HP and OA, for the opportunity to serve.

—November 2012

Reach for Recovery

I am a first time Region Seven Representative for my intergroup. Last weekend was a miracle for my growth. Every time I stretch outside my comfort zone, I learn something new and invaluable about my program and myself.

Yet every time a service opportunity presents itself, I waver and scramble for reasons why "I simply can't do that right now." The litany is long. This time my excuse was that I was without a sponsor for the first time in my four years in OA.

Still reeling from that sudden blow, I felt ungrounded and sad—almost as if a friend had passed away. But the more I worked my program around the issue, the more it became clear HP was moving me into a deeper level of awareness and more growth. By removing my crutch, HP showed me I needed to depend on him—first and always. He further clarified this at the Region Seven Assembly.

Don't misunderstand. I am far from advocating a no-sponsor system. I have already asked someone to be my temporary sponsor. I don't want to do this alone, but my dependence on my previous sponsor was unhealthy. She had become my HP in many ways, and it was time to examine that comfort zone.

To move through my loss and sadness, I needed to work my program and step up to service I had committed to earlier. Fearful, a bit lost, and very sad, I still believed HP had a plan. I chose trust and did what my sponsor had encouraged me to do every day—reach for recovery.

Upon arrival at the assembly, my character defects were raging—judgment, self-righteousness, arrogance, and impatience with the process and the attendees. I was tired, sad, frustrated, and, above all, lonely. It occurred to me this would be when I would call my sponsor. The realization I couldn't was overwhelming. Tears started as I reached for my journal.

I could only manage blurts of words: I'm so sad . . . . I miss my sponsor . . . . Poor me . . . . I'm so lonely!

With that last phrase, I heard a tapping on my hotel room door. Wiping away tears and reprimanding myself for the impending embarrassment, I opened the door. The OA member (whom I did not know well) looked at me and said, "Do you need a hug?" I collapsed into her arms and sobbed. She asked if I needed to talk. I shared my sadness, fears, and loneliness and found more strength and recovery than I had had in months.

The next day, I had a new mindset. A feeling of gratitude surrounded me. Thank God for these wonderful people who are abstinent and willing to do this service. Without them, I wouldn't have this program.

It's true what they say: When we are willing to give service, we receive much more in return. That weekend was life changing. Thanks to the mysterious way HP works, I will always feel a connection to the person who saved me from myself. And I have a stronger commitment to service. I need to be here. More important, I need to be here for the next compulsive overeater.

Thank you, HP and OA friends. It's the "we" part of this program that keeps me coming back. I used my Tools to reach out for help in my recovery, and HP sent an angel in skin. I don't think I would have been open to receiving that gift had I not been reaching for recovery in the first place.

Work your program. Reach for recovery. The miracles are there. All we need to do is be willing to receive them.

—May 2012

See You at WSBC!

I have been incredibly blessed by the service I've provided beyond my home meeting. It has given me the ability to feel my feelings and do things anyway. Fortunately, my sponsor encouraged me early on to get involved in our intergroup. I thought intergroup was only about business. Fear almost paralyzed me when I thought, "What on earth do I know about business?"

Reluctantly, I went. Within one of the first months, I remember our delegate returning from the World Service Business Conference (WSBC) and giving us such a passionate, inspiring, and encouraging report that I wanted to go to WSBC too! I never forgot her enthusiasm; it was contagious. I caught her "service bug" and followed in her footsteps just a few years later.

When someone asked me to consider a region representative position, my character defect of fear popped into my mind. I did not think I was capable or knowledgeable enough to do this type of service. Our wonderful region trustee told me, "God does not call the qualified; he qualifies the called." I believed her because of what I had seen her do. Early in program I remember someone telling me, "Look for what you want in a sponsor and ask how he or she is achieving it." I saw what our WSBC delegates had, and I knew I wanted it too. The region trustee was right about God qualifying me. OA is the safest place to learn and practice any new behavior or skill. Where else can you make a mistake and not feel that you *are* a mistake?

The more service I do and the more I give back what was given to me, the more I gain—and I don't mind this kind of gaining at all! It encourages me to maintain my abstinence, so I can be accountable to pursue these positions. Becoming a region representative and world service delegate has helped me increase my self-esteem each time I accomplish a task. I've gained self-respect by voicing my opinions and being treated with respect no matter what the outcome. I have also gained the opportunity to meet people from all over the world who have the same disease I do.

By doing these services, the OA promises come true. I challenge and encourage each of you to take the next step toward doing service at the region or world service levels. I hope I have infected many of you with the "service bug" I caught many years ago. We need to carry the message of experience, strength, and hope to the still-suffering compulsive overeater. It's our duty—and it's too much fun to pass up.

Hope to see you sometime soon in New Mexico!

—May 2009

Get a Sponsor

When I attended my first OA meetings, I was clueless. I came to lose weight. I thought I needed "the diet" that the folks in OA seemed to be using. Today I am thankful no one blessed me with "the diet." What I received instead was an open, honest sharing from the Fellowship. In those first meetings, folks shared recollections of their food thoughts and behaviors. Their stories very much resembled my own. Thank God, I was able to identify.

As I listened to the sharing and began to share a bit of my story, I often received feedback. Other members kept saying, "Go to as many meetings as possible. Listen for someone who has what you want and ask him or her how he or she got it." That thought is an oversimplified and conversational version of "get a sponsor."

I spent almost two years working the Fellowship rather than working the Steps. Finally I found a sponsor, and all that changed. I feel blessed that my first sponsor's abstinence was the most important thing in his daily living. In our earliest phone conversations, out of habit, I always said, "How are you doing?" His instant response was always, "I am abstinent." At first I thought he was just being cute. Today I realize that "abstinence first, without exception" is the only way to live recovery in serenity. I also realize he had to be living abstinence in recovery if he was to have any hope of sharing it.

In those early days, I had no idea I shared the blame for my failed relationships. It had not occurred to me I needed, among other things, spirituality, daily practice of our Tools, and a personal commitment to working the Twelve Steps. The thought that I needed to work on my resentments and character defects might have seemed important, if I thought I had any! But I thought all I needed was the right diet, and all I wanted to talk about in my early meetings with my sponsor was the food. I thank my Higher Power that my sponsor had sufficient patience and understanding to keep saying, "For today, let's continue our work on the Steps. That's how I got abstinent, and it is the path I am suggesting for you."

My sponsor was abstinent and never wavered from the Steps he had taken to get that way. I continued to whine as he guided me through the Steps, but work the Steps I did. Indeed, I was blessed with abstinence in the midst of that process. Thank God for abstinent sponsors.

—*February 2013*

Daily Contact Important

As I immersed myself in program after I arrived in OA over twenty-five years ago, I heard of the importance of sponsorship to my recovery.

Six weeks into my recovery, I attended an OA weekend event and heard many people share about their recoveries. A healthy-looking woman, who behaved in a sane manner and appeared free of compulsive eating, attracted me. This approach to life very much attracted me, and I asked her to be my sponsor. I'll always be grateful that she did sponsor me and helped me grow in recovery through our daily contact. Through her, I learned I could be abstinent no matter the circumstances. I could be free of compulsive overeating, could change, and could have choices. Before OA, the disease trapped me as soon as the compulsion hit; I never had choice. What a gift choice is!

My first sponsor and I had daily contact for seven years. My normal approach to life was to be a loner, figure things out myself, not ask questions, and pretend all was okay. To live abstinently I could no longer be like that. My daily contact taught me how to share with another, be honest, let another into my life, ask questions, figure out how to work the Steps, and be abstinent regardless of situations. Over the years I've changed sponsors a couple of times as circumstances have changed.

Today, sponsorship is as important to me as it was at the beginning of my OA journey. I need my sponsor to be immersed in OA, committed to abstinence, available to connect with me, and willing to challenge me to grow into all I can be (not that I'm always appreciative at first of searching questions or tasks).

Daily contact is still important to me. Now it's email that enables that contact, and video calls facilitate weekly "face-to-face" meetings. The daily connection with my sponsor means

I'm reflecting on happenings in my life and my responses, how I'm using the Steps, how much I'm seeking and following God's will, how grateful I am, and whether any compulsive thoughts or behaviors are trying to get back into my life. Our daily readers, *For Today* and *Voices of Recovery,* are wonderful prompts for reflection.

Today, my busy life makes it difficult for my sponsees to have the daily phone contact I experienced in my early recovery. I thought using electronic forms of communication wouldn't work for sponsorship, but experience has shown they can work and work well as an alternative when circumstances require it.

I am committed to sharing the gift of sponsorship with others, so they may know the gift of freedom I received and have choice in their lives not to pick up the food or compulsive eating behaviors.

—July 2013

Abstinent Sponsors

Abstinence is a commitment, a decision, and an action—of this I am aware. It is a commitment and a decision I made over thirty-four years ago. I've been taking the actions necessary a day at a time ever since. It has also been a surrender process. The more I surrendered, the more I realized freedom from food obsession. I learned early I would not be able to keep this priceless gift if I didn't share it.

My life began to take on a new meaning. The more I was abstinent, the more I wanted to be abstinent. Abstinent sponsors came into my life, sharing with me the need to work the Twelve Steps. I began to learn that this is a spiritual program.

Conscious contact with a power greater than me, one that guides me into actions that strengthen my commitment to abstinence, keeps me abstinent over the long haul. By reaching out to an abstinent sponsor, I am putting into action my commitment to abstinence and developing my spirituality. As a result, I live an abstinent life.

I learned that I had to give it back. Sponsorship, Twelfth Step work, and my relationship with the God of my understanding keep me abstinent. It is important in my abstinent life to practice the OA Twelve Traditions, especially Tradition Five. As our OA Preamble reads, "Our primary purpose is to abstain from compulsive eating and compulsive food behaviors and to carry the message of recovery through the Twelve Steps of OA to those who still suffer." Not only does abstinence allow me to receive a glorious life, it grants me a way to give back. One of the greatest joys of recovery comes to me when I share our OA program with other compulsive overeaters.

The spiritual awareness Principle continues to increase my understanding of the necessity of abstinent sponsors. I can't give what I don't have. The knowledge of God's will and the power to carry it out in my life is what gives me the strength to continue my commitment to abstinence and the actions I need to take to carry this life-giving, life-saving message to the next compulsive eater. As *The Twelve Steps and Twelve Traditions of Overeaters Anonymous* taught me, "Those of us who live this program don't simply carry the message; *we are the message*" (p. 106).

I am a grateful, abstinent sponsor. I am aware how important this is. For this I thank God, the OA program, and my beloved Fellowship of Overeaters Anonymous.

—January 2013

A Little Voice Said

Eight weeks ago, I attended my first OA meeting. I'd researched OA and vaguely knew about a concept of abstinence, but that was about it.

After a bit more reading, another meeting, and devouring the Big Book and OA *Twelve and Twelve*, I realized I urgently needed a sponsor. After all, from reading the *Twelve and Twelve*, it seemed I was already through Steps One through Three and needed to be getting on with Step Four. I could sense it might be insufficient to work that one alone, so I drew breath, gathered my courage, and found a sponsor.

In our first conversation, we talked a little, but before I could tell her how far along in the program I was, she asked me to read aloud the first paragraph of Step One. Then she asked which sentence resonated most with me. I pulled one out and read it back to her. She said, "Right. Go away and write about that for the next time we talk."

I wanted to say, "No, no, it's okay. I've done Step One. I accept I'm powerless over food and my life is unmanageable. I need and want God's help. Let's look at Step Four!" I didn't want to waste more time. Didn't she realize I'd been immersed in the material for two weeks and was a very fast learner? I was secretly horrified that if this was the pattern, it would take me at least two weeks to do Step One!

Something held me back. I knew she had more than twenty years of abstinence, and I wanted that too. And a little voice said, "Maybe you aren't such a fast learner. Maybe you should listen to someone vastly more experienced? Maybe not be such a know-it-all?" I took my sponsor's advice. I moved slowly through the paragraphs. I found there was so much to write about, and suddenly I didn't want to rush.

Eight weeks in, and I'm still on Step One. I'm in sight of

the final paragraph, but several miracles have occurred. I have experienced a beautiful abstinence without fear for the last five days. I have learned humility and patience. I have had time to meditate and reflect on the true implications of Step One.

When I first rushed through the chapter in my initial excitement, I grasped it intellectually. Now, I have come to believe it in my heart.

—*December 2014*

Living Miracles

I have been a newcomer to OA three times over the past twenty years. The final time was eight months ago after finally hitting bottom. Hopeless, I had no fight left in me; I surrendered. I knew I needed help, and God and OA were all that were left.

Having "tried" the program before without success, I knew I had to do things in a different way. This time I was willing to make an honest effort to work the Steps and Tools.

The most pressing Tool I needed was a sponsor. In true addict fashion, I was a bit compulsive about it. I went to a couple of meetings with the sole purpose of finding a sponsor. (I did drive-thru on the way to and from.) At the fifth meeting, I was listening with care as someone shared. Suddenly my brain said, "I want what he has." And I remembered that's what our literature says about getting a sponsor.

The next day I called him, leaving a message on his answering machine. But I'm an addict, so I want what I want when I want it. I turned to a phone meeting.

At the end of that meeting, the meeting leader asked sponsors to give their phone numbers, so I wrote them down. I knew if I didn't get a sponsor right away, I'd die. As soon as the meeting was over, I called one and asked how she went about sponsoring. She gave me a long list of rules about the relationship between her sponsees and herself, including that she would tell me what I could and could not eat. I wanted a sponsor that night, but somehow my insides were saying she wasn't the right one for me.

So I waited with a little more patience to talk to the man from the face-to-face meeting. When I asked him if he would sponsor me, he said, "Eat three meals a day, nothing in-between, get a copy of the Big Book, read to page 60, and call me." Somehow I knew that was the road to freedom for me. That was eight months ago, and I am so grateful that OA is big enough for all sorts of sponsor/sponsee relationships.

Today I am a living, breathing, walking miracle of this program. My weight has gone from 230 pounds (104 kg) to 180 pounds (82 kg), and my triglycerides went from 374 to 129. The relationship with my daughter has gone from a rollercoaster ride, with me causing the seasick feeling, to one with a levelheaded, sane mother who acts on life rather than reacts.

Do I owe it all to my sponsor? No! He would be the first to point that out. I owe it all to my Higher Power, who is doing for me what I can't do for myself. And HP has gifted me with a proven, workable method and a Fellowship full of people who help me and let me help them. That's what is so amazing! While I am grateful for all the help my sponsor is giving me, in reality I'm helping him in his recovery at the same time.

Thank you to all the sponsors throughout the OA world who share their experience, strength, and hope with those of us who are still suffering. Sponsors are living miracles who believe, even before we do, that the miracle can happen to us too!

—*September 2013*

7

TRADITIONS

Principle Focus

This morning, I picked up my OA *Twelve and Twelve* to read Tradition One because I needed help with a challenging situation at work. I know how well Tradition One works to keep meetings strong and united, and I needed help working as a team with a colleague.

When a conflict or difference of opinion comes up, Tradition One suggests, "we give other people's opinions a respectful hearing. We express our own opinions honestly without belittling those who may disagree" (*The Twelve Steps and Twelve Traditions of Overeaters Anonymous*, p. 111). After the discussion, "we resolve our differences of opinion by considering the welfare of the group as a whole" (*The Twelve Steps and Twelve Traditions of Overeaters Anonymous*, p. 111).

Tradition One teaches me to focus on Principles rather than differences. When I turn inward, my HP tells me that I am safe even if things don't look the way I think they should. Just like there is more than one approach to recovery, there is more than one approach to doing things at work. For today, for unity to exist at work, I need to refrain from focusing on and discussing differences.

I learned how to do this in OA group conscience meetings. After I share my opinion and the group decides to do something different, I support it because the unity of the group depends upon it, and my recovery depends on the unity of the group.

I want unity at work, in my marriage, and in my relationships, and Tradition One tells me how to achieve it: listen with an open heart, share my truth, come to a decision on what's best for all, and commit myself to following the group conscience. This takes a good deal of letting go for this recovering control freak, but sanity, abstinence, and recovery are worth it!

—January 2015

Spiritual Nourishment

I'm a grateful compulsive overeater who has been in OA for ten years. By the grace of a loving Higher Power and the Fellowship, I've been blessed with more than nine years of abstinence. I've lost 55 pounds (25 kg) and have kept it off for over six years. My home group alternates between studying a Step and a Tradition each month. I learn much from Tradition meetings.

The Second Tradition reminds me that a loving God, as expressed through the group conscience, is in charge of our OA groups. When I try to control how the meeting is run, my self-will is operating and not the group conscience. It's important for me to remember that I may voice my opinion about a topic but must also listen to others express their opinions.

What is a group conscience? According to *The Twelve Steps and Twelve Traditions of Overeaters Anonymous*, "The group conscience is not the same as majority rule. This conscience is an expression of the group unity spoken of in the first tradition, a common bond which grows among us as we each let go of self-will" (p. 120).

To have a true group conscience, I think it's crucial to let everyone in the group be heard in a group discussion, even if one or two people have unpopular opinions. I need to let go of self-will so I can hear what other members have to say. I grow a little when I can do this.

I find spiritual nourishment in giving back to OA. However, I think rotation of leadership is important because it keeps me humble and I need to let a service position go at some point. It keeps me from thinking that everyone in OA depends on me, and I'm the only one who knows how to do it right. Rotation of leadership means that I let go of a position after a designated amount of time, so someone else can give service.

The Second Tradition tells me we all have a chance to participate in this Fellowship and to express our opinions. When we all have a chance to express our views, then a fair group conscience can be formed. Most of the time the group's Higher Power, as expressed through the group conscience, includes loving consideration of every group member.

Thank you to everyone in OA. The life-transforming Principles in the Steps and Traditions have given me a life beyond my wildest dreams.

—*February 2009*

I Was Surprised

In January 2006, I walked into the OA rooms for the first time. I was at my top weight of nearly 200 pounds (91 kg). I preferred to spend time alone eating, rather than being with people. When I did break from the food, shame of being overweight kept me from going out with friends and enjoying life. I was desperate.

I don't know what I expected at my first meeting, but I was surprised at what I found. These people were thin and happy! I felt like I was in the wrong place, since I was overweight and depressed. When the meeting began, they read the *Twelve Steps and Twelve Traditions*. I listened more closely to those words than I have since. Tradition Three sounded too good to be true: The only requirement for OA membership is a desire to stop eating compulsively. I had met the requirement!

Because I was a newcomer, the group chose to read the First Step out of the OA *Twelve and Twelve*. Since then, I've heard many OA members share their stories and say they felt at home at their first meeting. I am no different. That day gave me such hope. It was the first time I felt comfortable in my own skin. I rejoiced at hearing the promises and had to hold back tears at the phrase, "Welcome to Overeaters Anonymous. Welcome home." For as long as I had been compulsively eating, I had the desire to stop. Now I have a place that accepts me and welcomes me just as I am.

—*March/April 2012*

Plays Well with Others

Have you ever been at a meeting and a leader or speaker begins by saying, "I know this isn't OA-approved literature, but . . ." and then reads a piece of non-OA-approved literature? Or, "I know [insert name] wouldn't mind if I shared this about her?"

Tradition Four states, "Each group should be autonomous except in matters affecting other groups or OA as a whole." Permitting outside literature and breaks of anonymity are two examples of harming OA groups or OA as a whole.

I've heard, "There are no musts in this program." However, according to our OA *Twelve and Twelve,* there is one: "Groups should not do anything which will injure other OA groups or OA as a whole" (*The Twelve Steps and Twelve Traditions of Overeaters Anonymous,* p. 137).

Our *Twelve and Twelve* explains that when people break Traditions, it's usually because they are uninformed, and members who are familiar with the Traditions have the responsibility to speak up. I find this extremely difficult; however, I've witnessed it several times.

Once, someone was going to read a religious version of the Steps. A courageous longtimer lovingly spoke up and requested that we stick to OA-approved literature. I am grateful because that might have harmed OA. A newcomer might think he must follow that particular path to recovery. It would be confusing.

I remember someone once broke my anonymity. It was difficult and disappointing. This doesn't mean that our meetings aren't safe places; it just means that, as members, we can help our own recovery and OA as a whole by studying and practicing the Traditions mindfully.

At first I thought the Traditions were just a set of boring rules. After many reading, Tradition studies, and conversations, I've learned how valuable and powerful they are. They help me function in my OA group, my marriage, my job—life! I am learning how to speak my truth with love, set boundaries, and surrender my will.

Now, after my sponsees work through the Twelve Steps, we move to the Traditions. God knows I need continual help in playing well with others.

—June 2014

Feeling Useful

My sponsor continually encourages me to look for and expect miracles in my everyday life. At first I was skeptical, but she's right. Living in recovery means a life beyond my wildest dreams. These miracles come in the most unlikely places.

Tradition Five in OA *Twelve and Twelve* says, "As we concentrate on carrying a message of hope to others, we are empowered to use our unique talents in ways that are truly useful to others. The result is better than any outcome we could have planned for ourselves, for we find a deep satisfaction in service as we join forces to share recovery in OA" (pp. 150-151). That has been my experience.

Who knew that feeling worthwhile, useful, and connected could feel better than compulsive eating? Recovery has taught me that, and I don't want to ever go back to disease behaviors.

I have so many opportunities to carry the message to the compulsive overeater who still suffers. Even if there isn't a newcomer at a meeting to talk with, there are longtime members who still suffer.

When someone is in relapse or struggling, helping that person is also the group's primary purpose. Just like Our Invitation to You says, "It is weakness, not strength, that binds us to each other...." (*Overeaters Anonymous, Third Edition*, p. 4).

I finally get why our group's primary purpose is to carry the message to those who still suffer. It doesn't matter how long I've been abstinent, I still need to hear the message, and I can't keep it unless I give it away. I am so grateful for this brilliant program! It works when we work it!

—June 2014

Marketing Missteps

My husband and I run a small business that supports us, even in a down economy, because we're diligent about marketing. We put our logo on just about anything. We sponsor charity events. We buy give-away bookmarks, magnets, and even temporary tattoos. We never leave home without twenty-five or more business cards, and we put cards in every piece of mail we send, including bills and birthday cards. Early on, I tripped over Tradition Six before I learned to put self-promotion away during meetings.

The first mistake I made was to be "helpful" by bringing a dozen of my business pens to our journaling meeting. A group member noticed and asked me some questions about my company. Later I realized it could appear like OA was endorsing me when those pens ended up mixed in with our meeting supplies. I replaced them with generic pens and tried to remember, "to place principles before personalities" (Tradition Twelve).

My next flub was bringing my company water bottle to the meeting. It sat on the table, proudly announcing my company's name, while others shared and listened to OA stories. When I realized, I put it on the floor. At future meetings, I replaced it with a plain water bottle.

But I caught myself before the next misstep. I decided I would serve by purchasing several OA *Twelve and Twelve* books to give to newcomers free of charge, and darn if I didn't go right for a tool my company owns that crimps "A gift from [business name]" onto the book. Not putting my company's name on something I was giving away went against every marketing bone in my body!

So, as much as it pains me to miss the fabulous marketing opportunities OA groups offer, I agree that Tradition Six protects OA from the disasters that can arise when money, property, and prestige are involved. I can promote my business on my own time, and thanks to the health I have gained in Overeaters Anonymous, I have more energy to do so.

—*June 2012*

Financial Peace

A suggested donation of $3 for threefold recovery . . . we have a threefold disease that affects us physically, emotionally and spiritually" ("Contributions to Recovery," *Lifeline*, June 2009, p. 12).

The Seventh Tradition is one of my favorite topics because my first contact with OA was through the OA website (oa.org). Where would I be if you had not contributed to the World Service Office so the OA website could be created and maintained? Thank you for realizing it is better to spend money to support your own recovery (and that of so many others) than to squander it feeding the disease.

I have a history of overdraft charges. My bank closed an account of mine because of my irresponsible spending. When I came into OA, I was 240 pounds (109 kg) and climbing, and I had $30,000 in unsecured debt accumulated during a year spent on eating, drinking, traveling, and shopping. I was "living the life," or so I thought.

About a year into my recovery, I surrendered my finances to my Higher Power. I was given financial steps to follow while I continued to work the Twelve Steps. My finances made a gradual fall into order. Today I tithe with joy (10 percent of my gross income) and smile when I pay my bills, which I do early. I am even saving money each month. I don't fear looking at my checking account because I am no longer spending what I don't have. I have financial peace. Financial insecurity has slipped away, not because I have more money, but because I stopped spending compulsively.

I thank my Higher Power and the Seventh Tradition for teaching me financial responsibility. So after reading the *Seventh Tradition of OA* pamphlet, I was glad to increase my contributions from $2 to $3 a meeting. I will continue to give more because you were there for me and gave as though your lives depended on it, before I knew mine did. I am committed to doing my part to support OA so it remains viable for the next compulsive eater. Thank you for your service to OA!

Here are some questions to ponder: Do you provide regular support to OA with your financial contributions? Are you spending compulsively? Have you seen a relationship between abstinence and your spending? Have you surrendered your finances to your Higher Power? Are you financially responsible today?

—July 2011

The Healing Power of Reciprocity

One of the most healing aspects of the OA program for me is the nonprofessionalism expressed in Tradition Eight. The mutual caring and sharing in the OA Fellowship have helped to open me up and enabled me to speak honestly with another human being for the first time in my life.

My first sponsor seemed very strange to me when I met her at my first meeting. She spoke honestly about her struggles and her defects and how the Principles of the Steps and Traditions helped her with them. I recognized in her something I wanted, even though she seemed to have more problems than anyone sitting around the table.

As our relationship grew, her candor encouraged me to become more open and honest, and I decided to share my Fourth and Fifth Steps with her. When I struggled to tell her something that I thought was so painfully, shamefully unique to me, this woman reassured me that I was not alone and recounted a similar episode from her own experience.

My ego didn't like it. I wanted to be unique. I regarded her mutual sharing as one-upmanship. I thought she was just unwilling to recognize what a special individual I was. But I gradually came to see that I needed this reciprocal dialogue. Not only did I learn that my life and problems were not unique, but I learned to accept them as a part of my humanness. I began to heal.

Through our relationship, I learned to relax and be myself. I felt she accepted everything I said and did. I felt free from judgment and condemnation. This was a first for me. And it was so eye-opening to witness someone who did not pretend to be perfect, but who rather used the spiritual Principles to grow through the problems in her life. She modeled a whole new way of living.

When my sponsor moved, I couldn't lean on her for strength and reassurance anymore. God was taking away my crutches so that I would come to rely only on him. I finally realized the truth of what my sponsor had been saying: I had to give of myself and carry a message of hope to others if I was to keep my own recovery.

I was scared at first, so I worked the Steps on my fear. I found another sponsor. Again, God led me to someone who unselfishly and caringly gives of herself. And, as I grew, I began to sponsor others. I've found that I need the benefits to my own program that only service—unselfish giving—can provide.

So when someone says, "Oh, you helped me so much just by listening," or "I'm glad to hear that you felt the same way I do," I know it is our Eighth Tradition in action.

—*August 2009*

Questioning Breaks

Recently I attended OA meetings where Tradition breaks occurred. Some people would prefer I say, "the meetings were not in harmony with the Traditions," but I prefer "traditions being broken" as written in *The Twelve Steps and Twelve Traditions of Overeaters Anonymous* (p.179). The real question for me is, "What am I willing to do when in the presence of a Tradition break?" For example, what should I do if a member reads from an outside source, refers to a weight-loss or treatment center by name, or ignores a meeting's guidelines?

Tradition Nine (and Tradition One) have guided me in a personal growth experience. In the past, it has been painful and frightening to speak up. I would think, "I'm new to the area. People might not like me. I am not well versed in the Traditions. What's the big deal anyway? I'll say something next time." I have studied, read, and done service at Tradition meetings as well as at the intergroup, region, and world-service levels. Suddenly God was doing for me what I could not do for myself. HP gave me the words to lovingly state at the end of the meeting what may not have been in harmony with the Traditions.

The OA *Twelve and Twelve* goes on to state, "Most veteran OA members have found that standing up for our traditions is worth the risk that we'll be criticized or that meetings might be 'less than serene.' The alternative could be something worse for us than temporary unpopularity and conflict.... Living by OA's ninth tradition means that we don't depend on some authority or power structure to enforce the traditions. We all take responsibility to speak out when they are being ignored" (p.181).

I am grateful that I am no longer afraid to speak up, always keeping in mind that Tradition Nine also tells me, "Once we have spoken our minds, however, the ninth tradition tells us to relax and let our Higher Power take charge of the meeting. We find we cannot force our will on the OA group, no matter how right it may seem to us" (*The Twelve Steps and Twelve Traditions of Overeaters Anonymous*, p. 182).

Questioning Traditions breaks is not a take-it-or-leave-it action. On pages 182 to 183 in the *Twelve and Twelve*, nine questions help us inventory how well we practice Tradition Nine. The seventh question asks, "*Are we afraid to speak up when we see traditions being ignore in our OA group?*" Surely it asks us to put personal fears aside and not be afraid to preserve the integrity of any Tradition not respected in our presence.

I am grateful to be a member of OA for thirty-two years and grateful to those who have questioned me about preserving the Traditions. This motivates me to write and continue to learn. I pray for the courage to continue to speak up.

—*September/October 2012*

Just Listen!

Recently, I was at a meeting where the topic was "What's one thing you've learned from program?" A myriad of things went through my head! How could I pick just one lesson from the last seven years?

In this meeting, each person reads a Step in turn, and then the Traditions are read; the remaining people introduce themselves. I read Tradition Ten, and as I passed the sheet to the woman next to me, it hit me. This was it! This was the number one thing I'd learned from the program! It was a double-HP whammy for me because, before then, if someone had asked me how the Traditions fit into my life and recovery, I wouldn't have been able to peg anything. Boy, was I blown away!

Before recovery, holy cow, did I have opinions on out-side issues! I couldn't keep my mouth shut to save my life. It seemed I spent 85 percent of my emotional and mental energy on stuff that was none of my business. I was in the business of everybody else's business. For my first six months of recovery, every person sharing in a meeting had my rapt attention, and my mind was going fourteen million miles an hour. For each thing a person said, I had five answers for him or her. After the meeting I couldn't wait to tell each person how to fix his or her life, and I'd stay an hour or longer doing just that. It was exhausting. I quickly learned not to.

Now my meetings are for me; I am there for my own re-covery, not everyone else's. I learned that fellowship can be a soft quiet togetherness.

Having opinions on outside issues was one of my top forms of insanity. Learning to just listen and be present for others was a major step into the sanity of recovery. Now I have 100 percent of my mental and emotional energy available to me, instead of it leaking all over the place. My feelings no longer overwhelm me when I listen to others, and I am sure they no longer overwhelm others. I am so grateful for my HP's magical way of showing up in marvelous and unexpected ways and for the gifts of the program. Keep coming back; it works if you work it!

—*September/October 2006*

Anna Nimity

I'm a compulsive overeater. By the grace of my Higher Power and the power of the Twelve Steps, I'm blessed to be abstinent for nineteen years and six months and have given away about 55 pounds (25 kg).

I had trouble saying "anonymity" until my first sponsor suggested I say it like a woman's name: Anna Nimity. Anonymity is important to my spiritual state and to our Fellowship as a whole.

"When we all respect the anonymity of others, we can trust that nobody outside these rooms will know we're coming to OA unless we tell them ourselves" (*The Twelve Steps and Twelve Traditions of Overeaters Anonymous*, p. 200). So it's okay for me to tell you I'm in OA. But if I see an OA member at a party or a public place and someone asks me how I know this person, it's not okay for me to say OA. I usually say the person is a friend of a friend and then change the subject. Also, it's not okay for me to repeat what I've heard in a meeting or on the telephone to someone outside of the meeting or the call. Instead, I share the joy and sanity I receive from this Fellowship by trying to be an example.

For a few years, I was blessed to be the public information chair at our intergroup. We got the word out to our community by holding public information events, hosting booths at street fairs, and getting public service announcements out to local radio and television stations. When we planned these events and activities, our committee made sure that the organizations we contacted knew we didn't want our faces or last names publicized—only that OA can help someone who has a problem with food.

I've also been blessed to go to several conventions, which is a great way to carry the message to our community. During conventions, the reading of an anonymity statement always precedes the featured speakers. This notifies anyone from the media that they can let the community know about our Fellowship but cannot show faces or mention last names.

This how we emphasize the Principles of our program and not personalities. This is carrying the message that OA can help you if you have a problem with food.

I am grateful I grew spiritually from giving back to OA in this way. It filled me up in a way that food never did. Service is my gratitude in action.

—*November 2014*

I Want to Reach Out

When we share our personal histories at meetings and with other OA members, we understand that anonymity is an OA hallmark and an important part of our recovery. But I have made a personal choice to relinquish my anonymity so I may reach out to others who are still suffering. I want to share with enthusiasm my knowledge of and experiences in the program. And I want others to know how it has helped me as I recover from compulsive overeating.

Because of my honesty with friends and strangers alike, several people with whom I have shared my story are now checking out OA's website (oa.org) and requesting literature. Many others have started to attend meetings regularly.

I carry several pamphlets with me at all times and keep them in my vehicle to hand out to people who request information about OA. One of my favorite pamphlets is titled, *Compulsive Overeating: An Inside View.* One of the last lines in this informational booklet is, "There is help." These words have given comfort and hope to me, and to many others.

I am grateful for this program and for living my life in abstinence in a healthy manner.

—December 2011

8

RECOVERY FROM RELAPSE

My End of the Bargain

I came to OA the first time in 1987 at 181 pounds (82 kg). I left in 1995 at 213 pounds (97 kg). A couple of times during that eight year period I got down to 140 pounds (64 kg), but I never stayed there long. Staying abstinent was too much work. I struggled with abstinence for many years because I wanted and expected it to be easy. I figured if I was doing my part, using the Tools and working the Steps, then God was supposed to do his part and "strike me abstinent." It didn't work out that way most of the time. Abstinence was not easy, so I sidestepped it, became discouraged, and left.

Today I pulled out one of my old OA journals and read about my early days in program. I had many entries about "God not holding up his end of the bargain." It never occurred to me that abstinence might be hard work. If I had a food thought, I felt God was letting me down.

Something finally clicked for me when I came back into program in April 2003 at 235 pounds (107 kg). Just before that, I had dieted down to 225 pounds (102 kg) from my top weight of 242 pounds (110 kg), but I was on my way back up the scale yet again. I knew 250 pounds (114 kg) was right around the corner, and then 300 pounds (136 kg).

During that time, I read in AA literature that Dr. Bob had frequent cravings for alcohol right up until his death in 1950, but he never had another drink after he became sober in 1935. That statement helped me to understand that I could pray for the willingness to do whatever I needed to do to recover from compulsive overeating and God would grant me the willingness, but that didn't mean it would be easy.

I had to put down the fork. It wasn't easy, and I had many white-knuckle minutes, hours, days, and weeks, but I kept praying, using the Tools, and working the Steps. I wrote down my food and committed it to my sponsor each morning. Some nights I would go to bed at 7:30 p.m. just so I wouldn't be tempted to eat. Food thoughts stayed with me constantly, but I finally realized that just because I had those thoughts didn't mean I had to act on them. What a concept!

Today (eighteen months later), I am maintaining a normal body weight of 135 pounds (61 kg), and I am at peace with food most of the time. I enjoy my abstinent meals, and I don't feel deprived because I don't eat sweets. Inappropriate food or eating behaviors sometimes call to me, but that no longer means God is not upholding his end of the bargain. It usually means I have some stuff going on that I need to look into.

I can sit on my hands if that's what I need to do to stay abstinent. God will give me the willingness to sit on my hands, pick up the phone, go to a meeting, read, pray, or whatever it is I need to do to stay abstinent, because I ask him for that willingness every morning and thank him for it every night. It may not always be easy, but it is always worth the effort.

—*April 2005*

Perseverance

P erseverance is the most important Step Principle in my recovery because OA is not a quick fix or a short-term diet program. By making OA and working the Steps a way of life, I have a new opportunity every day—every hour if necessary—to start over and keep moving in a positive direction.

Perseverance is important when I am emotionally, spiritually, and physically on track, and even more important when I am struggling.

After significant losses in my personal life, I went through relapse. I am grateful and fortunate that the physical aspect of my relapse was mild. However, the emotional and spiritual relapses were challenging.

I firmly believe the Principle of perseverance kept me linked to the OA program throughout my period of grief and relapse. My mantra, which I often shared in meetings, became, "Show up, tell the truth, and keep trying." I came to meetings no matter what, spoke honestly about how I was doing with my emotions and food, and continued to work each Tool to the best of my ability.

Over six months later, I emerged again from my obsession with food. Now I am again abstinent and closely connected with my Higher Power. I enjoy the serenity resulting from putting down both the food and obsessive thinking about food. OA works if we just stay connected, do our best, and draw upon the support of the Fellowship. Perseverance means never quitting the program no matter how bumpy the path may be.

It is best summed up with our slogan, "Don't quit before the miracle happens." Don't quit after the miracle happens either! Recovery is not a linear process; new challenges emerge to work through. I can withstand anything and come out stronger if, in partnership with my Higher Power, I just persevere in working the Tools and Steps of the OA program.

—September/October 2008

The Impossible Happens

Listening to OA members' stories, again and again one hears, "I didn't think it was possible." Members would say it was not possible for them to lose weight, stop bingeing, improve relationships, cope with problems, or find balance in their lives. Yet after working the OA program, the same people proclaim these good things did happen.

How can this be? I, too, scoffed and did not believe the promises were possible. I questioned, challenged, and dared not believe in success. I could not stand, yet again, to set myself up for failure. Then last year I returned to OA after being away for twenty-seven years.

Desperation brought me to a meeting; but a sponsor, the Big Book, and other people in the program kept me coming back. They offered me support and hope.

With the help of OA members and my Higher Power, one day at a time, I move toward achieving "my impossible." Just one year ago I considered the changes in my thinking, eating, and body as impossible dreams.

To the still-suffering compulsive overeater, with gratitude and humility I say, "The OA program makes the impossible happen."

—May 2008

Little Miracle

It is nearly 10 p.m. Less than four hours ago, I was not sure I would make it through the night with my abstinence intact. I am again new to abstinence and must go through the physical withdrawal and mental obsession that are so difficult early on.

My first instinct is to fight, to will my way through it. But that doesn't work, and if it does, it doesn't work for long. I called my sponsor instead. She wasn't there, so I left a message. I called another OA member and left a message. There were no face-to-face OA meetings scheduled tonight, so I attended an

AA meeting.

As I sat listening to the speaker, I felt like I was going to come out of my skin. What was I going to do about the food? I wanted to go to a fast-food drive-thru. Sure, I'd get food that wasn't safe for me to eat, but it wouldn't be sugar if I didn't get a soda. It would be a meal, and it would be better than bingeing. But would I be able to stop? Or after completing my fast-food meal, would I decide that a bag of candy, a box of cookies, or a few candy bars might be okay too? Would it be enough? Is it ever enough?

In the past, I might not have called my sponsor or gone to a meeting in the first place. A few days ago, I wasn't willing to take even these small steps to take care of myself. When this urge has hit me, I've given in, or I've willed myself through it. Either way I'm miserable. Using willpower only postpones the inevitable. Higher Power be thanked; tonight I had a little fight left in me.

So I prayed. I told my Higher Power I wasn't capable, and if it were up to me, I'd go to the fast-food place. No way was I staying abstinent on my own.

If I was going to get through this, my Higher Power would have to do it. At the AA meeting I thought, "If I go to the drive-thru, then that's just what I do. If I binge, I binge. I can't choose. I can't do this."

I was so jittery that I left the meeting a few minutes early. Walking to my car, I still didn't know what I was going to do. After all my footwork in the program, would I wind up blowing it and bingeing? Would I end up enduring another night of misery because I was once again confronted with my hopelessness? Would I have to lie to comfort myself, making resolutions to start again tomorrow? That elusive tomorrow—does it ever come?

My Higher Power came through and told me what to do. My Higher Power told me where to get a safe meal, one I could look forward to eating and enjoy. I went to a vegetarian restaurant and ordered a to-go meal, still a little unsure of myself, but thankful I was making this choice.

As if that weren't miracle enough, when I got home and opened the to-go containers, I decided I wouldn't eat all the food. It was more than one meal, and I would save the rest to take to work tomorrow. And I did. Wow! Just a couple of hours before, I considered giving in to the disease and giving up my abstinence.

My sponsor told me if I focus on the Steps and the Tools, my food would fall into place. I've spent so much time focusing on food; the truth is I can have a perfect food plan, but what good does it do me if I'm not able to follow it? A few days ago, I wasn't able to follow it. But today I did footwork: I read from the Big Book, I did some writing, I prayed, I made phone calls, and I went to a meeting. I was willing, and my Higher Power came through for me when I couldn't come through for myself.

As I type this, I am grateful. I am not cured of this disease or guaranteed abstinence tomorrow. I have problems that seem impossible to overcome; I am still rebelling inside and holding back from working this program to the best of my ability. But today I experienced a little miracle in spite of all this—proof this program does work if you work it, even a little.

—*December 2009*

Hope and Grief

How do I maintain hope, no matter what I have to deal with? First, I accept that my Higher Power will give me only what I can handle and no more. At these moments, it is clear HP knows I can deal with much more than I anticipated. Acceptance is always the basis, no matter the situation.

In fourteen years with OA, I have lost my abstinence only once. I have maintained it the last four years despite dealing with severe physical injuries and emotional blows that have rocked my world. I briefly lost the ability to walk, but I re-learned it despite the specialist predicting I'd never get past the wheelchair.

My emotional pain includes the fears and insecurities that go with the loss of a gift I took for granted: walking. And the death of my father was not easy. When my beloved husband was diagnosed with cancer in June 2005 and passed away in October 2005, I was terrified. I was also abstinent.

For me, abstinence is far more important than anything or anyone. Without it, I would be 400 pounds (182 kg) and still stuck in a hospital bed. Today, I'm within 60 pounds (27 kg) of my goal weight, and I can walk and even dance, as I did at our regional convention in July 2006.

Our Tools, especially writing and the telephone, have been vital for me. I use both Tools daily to maintain contact with my sponsors, those I sponsor, and any member who shares his or her address. Writing allows me to release the fears and share the hope in ways in which spoken words fail me.

Rereading letters consistently enriches me while permitting my bold and controlling sense of self to finally step aside. Love, wisdom, friendships, trust, and hope pour not only from my pen but also from those who take the time to be there for others. What a gift we share.

Reading *For Today, Voices of Recovery, Lifeline,* and the *Twelve and Twelve* reminds me I am not alone. For me, that is a need, not a want. The freedom of choice to read the Big Book, *Lifeline Sampler, Beyond Our Wildest Dreams,* or *Overeaters Anonymous* is a gift as well.

When my husband spent thirty-two days in the hospital, I loaded up his truck with my OA books, stationery, stamps, envelopes, and address book. While he slept, underwent tests, or had an operation, I wrote or read. Writing took concentration and made me less aware of time passing.

The last forty-eight hours of his life, I was never alone. Once we were home, I called an old OA friend to let her know. She called others. Within two hours, members were at our door. Some came and went for short periods of time; others stayed until he passed away, to help me deal with his death.

I still write and telephone, go to three to seven meetings a week, sponsor, and work with my sponsor. I utilize each Tool. I remain on the service board and serve in two meetings. When requested, I speak at meetings and conventions. My food plan remains flexible, as my doctors suggested. When cravings strike at the most unexpected times, the joy of writing is the greatest Tool I know to use at those points.

Reading and occasionally sharing our literature is never dull, and it creates a stir by adding new viewpoints, especially while conversing with newcomers. It's such a breath of fresh air.

—December 2006

Bright Lights of OA

My anorexic/bulimic mind kept me from Overeaters Anonymous for a long time because I thought it meant "Overweights Anonymous."

As a child, I refused to eat for days at a time; that is, until I found sweets and bingeing. Like many anorexic/bulimic people, I was an overachiever. I debuted in a Broadway show at age 21 and traveled with the jet set during my three years on stage and in film. Eventually the overwork, overexercise, overeating, and starving cut my feet from under me. Injuries prevented me from using exercise to purge, and I turned to vomiting.

An obese friend joined OA, but I didn't think it was for me because I was not overweight. A 5-foot-9-inch (175-cm) man, I weighed 118 pounds (54 kg). Later I went down to 108 pounds (49 kg) and thought, "I'm almost rid of my potbelly." After I binged, I would think, "I'm glad that's over; I'll never do that again," only to find myself rummaging through cupboards at 3 a.m. looking for something to fill that hole inside that told me life was empty and meaningless. I would starve myself for days. This cycle went on endlessly.

One day my OA friend called, and by this time she was healthy. I told her about my secret life. She said I would be welcome at OA meetings. Unlike in my performing career, I was not an immediate success in OA—probably because this program requires humility, a quality unfamiliar to me. People feared for my life.

I finally surrendered to my Higher Power, worked the Steps, and started helping others. This gave me a new life. My OA friends have supported me all the way. I have had seven years of healthy eating, normal weight, and freedom from bingeing, vomiting, starving, and overexercise. The gift of abstinence remained, even through five surgeries on tendons strained and damaged by muscle wasting, a side effect of being underweight.

Gone are the glittering lights of Broadway and Hollywood, but God's light has replaced them. Today I am back in university and spending my spare time helping sponsees work the Steps. This program has given me a daily reprieve and the absolute certainty that my life is a success if I abstain from compulsive eating today. Thank you, OA, for welcoming all compulsive eaters.

—*March/April 2006*

Special Gift

I have been in OA for seven years. I'm 73 years old and diabetic. My food problems started at birth. I was on a diet from age 10 until I found OA.

When I found OA, I was on a diabetic food plan and jumped right into program. I knew this was the answer. I found a sponsor (the same one I still have, bless her), started doing the Steps, and attended two meetings a week. I lost a considerable amount of weight, and all was well with the world until . . .

Last year, I was involved in two automobile accidents. My world changed—I changed. I had been abstinent for six years and hadn't eaten my favorite food, just one of my triggers, during that time. My first thought after the first accident was, "I could be dead, and I never would have had ice cream again!"

When I was able, I went right out and had a cone. Of course I thought, "That's not too bad." But before long it became a compulsion to have it every day. Before long, I added my other triggers back in. It's amazing how quickly that first bite turned into a year of relapse.

Throughout my relapse I never left the rooms, of course. But I wasn't honest with my sponsor, anyone at meetings, or myself. I believed they couldn't notice the 30 pounds (14 kg) I had gained. I felt that at my age I should eat what I wanted; I deserved that much.

On May 1, 2010, after much prayer, I surrendered to God. By the grace of God, I received my precious gift of abstinence back. I know it wasn't my persistence. God led me, and I realized the special gift: my abstinence.

I am joyous, happy, and free once again. I'm honest with my sponsor, everyone at meetings, and myself. I have lost half of my weight gain. I'm doing extra work with my sponsor each week, doing more telephoning, and being more active at the gym. I've got my life back. I'm vigilant with my gift of abstinence, guarding it as something precious, one day at a time.

—*September/October 2011*

Relapse Stepping-Stones

A list came across my desk, describing what I would call stepping-stones to relapse. Since my abstinence has been good for almost four years, I didn't give the list much thought. I have been so busy being busy, I considered myself safe from the harm of slipping and eventual relapse. Among the stepping-stones were some character defects to which I could relate: exhaustion, dishonesty, impatience, argumentativeness, depression, frustration, self-pity, cockiness, complacency, too high expectations of others, lax disciplines, use of mood altering chemicals, too many wants, loss of gratitude, unrealistic "it can't happen to me" thinking, and omnipotence.

Wow! What a list. I'm a lifelong compulsive overeater who has used every one of these excuses for not working my program. If I were to address these stepping-stones, I would say, "Oh, I'm exhausted from the service I do. I deserve a treat." But am I exhausted or just feeling sorry for myself, i.e. self-pity and unappreciated? Is this what's really going on, or am I being dishonest or impatient, not taking the time to pray and meditate?

I would rather be argumentative. Having been in program for a long time, I realize this thinking frustrates me. Frustration often leads to depression because I want things to go my way and don't want to feel like I'm not okay. Inevitably, my alter ego steps in thinking she will save the day. I get cocky and think I know better than others. I can slip into being judgmental. I become complacent and begin letting up on disciplines that remind me to take care of the weeds in my own garden and not worry about others' gardens. Prayer and meditation go out the window. Before I know it, I am looking for mental and physical diversions to keep the focus off myself.

When I'm not keeping the focus on myself, I am at risk of becoming judgmental and expecting too much from others. My priorities become askew, and I think how nice some junk food would taste. Luckily, my Higher Power steps in and reminds me how these mood-altering treats have sent me on a path of no return, where a slip would become a relapse. I've been there and done that, when I want too much but am unwilling to put the effort into working for the peace and serenity abstinence has always given me.

So as I ruminate on my life's landscape, I remember the "sunlight of the Spirit" (*Alcoholics Anonymous,* 4th ed., p. 66) and my gratitude for the gifts OA has given me. Most important, I must remember that slips and relapse are more likely when I sport the attitude that it can't happen to me. I am not omnipotent. Only God is. I have a Higher Power, but I am not my Higher Power. So as long as I practice the OA Twelve Steps and Twelve Traditions and do service to the best of my ability, I will have the strength and courage to walk the path and avoid the stepping-stones to relapse.

—September/October 2011

Now I Know

When I first came to OA, I read the literature, attended one meeting a week, avoided using a food plan, was deathly afraid of the 1,000-pound (454-kg) telephone, attended church, and was afraid to get a sponsor.

Over the years, I increased my meeting attendance to twice a week, studied the literature, created a food plan but wouldn't use it, started making phone calls, changed churches, got a cosponsor, and began to sponsor.

At my ten year mark, I was getting bored with the program and knew I was at a crossroads in my recovery. I had been maintaining a healthy weight but wanted to kick it into high gear and drop at least 10 pounds (5 kg). I changed meetings, went to a nutritionist, got a new sponsor, committed my food every morning (and would not change it come hell or high water), made three calls a day, journaled on questions given to me by my sponsor, began overexercising, and lost 25 pounds (12 kg). I was obsessed with losing weight and became underweight. I got scared, quit OA, and started eating.

After experiencing a five-year relapse and a 45-pound (21-kg) weight gain, I came back with a renewed appreciation for Overeaters Anonymous. I was willing to do whatever I had to do to get recovery.

I began by attending four meetings a week, and still do, two years later. I have committed to a healthy food plan and use it, not over- or undereating. I quit church attendance but have a strong spiritual program. I read three to four recovery-based readings in the morning and another three to four in the evening with my husband, who is now an active member of OA. I have lost 25 pounds (12 kg), am back at a healthy weight, and am maintaining it by the grace of God and the support of OA. I have a sponsor, and I sponsor many people. Every time a new member asks me to sponsor him or her, I chuckle to myself, thinking HP must believe I need more support. I give service, but I am careful not to overdo it.

I believe my relapse has made my recovery more credible and relatable to others. I feel more well-rounded and grateful for my recovery. I cherish my newfound abstinence, and I understand I must keep it if I am going to sponsor others.

I have found freedom in OA to change things if they are not working for me. By being honest with others and myself, I can identify trouble spots and make the necessary changes. I now know quitting OA is not the answer. The answer is in being honest and asking for help within the Fellowship until I get what I need to recover.

—*November 2013*

9

RECOVERY AROUND THE WORLD

Heavy Burden

When I was overeating, I carried a huge sack on my back. Every time I had a binge, I would put a big rock in my sack. That rock was called "guilt." Many times I promised I would not overeat again. And each time I overate, I had to put a rock of guilt into my already heavy sack.

I had to tell lies to cover my guilt. For each lie, I had to add a big rock called "lie" to my sack. Every time I told a lie, I had to remember the lie and to whom I had told it, so I could maintain the deceit. So for every lie I told, I also had to add a big rock called "fear" (of being found out) into the massive sack on my back. Bingeing was so selfish. I spent all our money on my food, wasted so much time eating, and missed out on my family growing up. For that I had to add rocks of selfishness and more guilt to my sack.

If carrying the extra weight on my body, the cholesterol and fat in my blood vessels, and the other ailments were not bad enough, I also had to drag this burdensome sack with me everywhere.

On their own, the weight of the obese body and sack of rocks were bearable. But the rocks had voices, crazy voices. They were constant—arguing, shouting, screaming, and demanding in those screechy, selfish voices. I couldn't concentrate. I couldn't sleep. I wished they would be quiet. Be quiet!

The only way to quiet the voices was to give them food—plenty and fast! Stuff it down! After they ate they would doze, and peace would come. But more rocks and voices would join my sack. The sack got heavier, the voices got louder, and the need to eat increased.

My problem was not food. My problem was thinking my solution was food. Some days I took the rocks out of the sack and sat on the big pile. It was precarious balancing on the guilt, lies, deceit, and selfishness. But from up there, everyone believed my lies. I could control what others believed about me. I was king of the world.

Other days, I was under the pile. The weight of the rocks would crush down on me, forcing the air from my lungs. I was unable to breathe or move. I couldn't see my survival beyond the next few seconds.

Then one day, the crushing weight on my chest and lack of breath were real. My heart had had enough. I was experiencing the symptoms of a heart attack. Knowing some first aid (a little knowledge is a dangerous thing), I decided the next best thing to do was get some aspirin. The store where I bought the aspirin had chocolate on sale. I washed down aspirin and chocolate with a cola. When I got to the hospital, the staff asked if I had eaten. I told them about the aspirin but not about the chocolate or cola. They could not understand my high blood sugar. I had to add more rocks of lies and guilt to my sack, and two more crazy voices entered my brain.

The doctor told me I was lucky to have survived and needed to lose weight. He never told me I had to empty the sack full of guilt, lies, fear, and selfishness. He never told me I had to silence the crazy voices in my brain. Through Overeaters Anonymous I found my HP, and he removed my rocks and voices.

Thank you all. Thank you, HP.

—England, September/October 2011

Free of the Scale

Recovery is many things. I came into program twenty-one years ago, desperate to find a way to stop bingeing and starving. I was never very overweight, but I found it harder and harder to fight the daily mental battle about my weight and food. Of course, only I knew this. Outside appearances said that here was a woman who had it all together. Recovery is personal, and I've received many gifts. Some came freely, and some came from hard work on the Steps and Tools.

By working the Steps and Traditions for twenty-one years, I've learned who I am, what I'm good at, what I like, what makes me happy, and whom I like to spend time with. I've also learned God is at the center of this self-knowledge. It's a fantastic feeling to be okay with myself and to have self-confidence and courage. As I continue to work the Steps, I continue to recover on all three levels (physical, emotional, and spiritual). I believe that if I'm not recovering on all three levels, I need to take a long, hard look at my program. Physical recovery is important to me. It's about reaching and maintaining a healthy and normal body weight.

When I came to OA, I met people who had recovery on all three levels. I needed to see that, especially the long-term weight loss and maintenance. As a newcomer, this proved to me the program worked. As a longtime abstainer and maintainer with nineteen years of back-to-back abstinence, part of my service is to carry a message of threefold recovery to newcomers and struggling longtimers.

I have learned how to live life free of the scale. For many years, the scale controlled my self-worth. Today, part of my recovery is to weigh myself infrequently. I am amazed at the freedom this has brought me. By staying away from the scale, I'm just me, and the only number I have to think about is my age!

What a joy to know that everything in my wardrobe fits. How pleasing it is to feel I deserve to have and wear nice clothes. I don't have a perfect body, but I can dress well and feel good about how I look.

Recovery means that when I attend a social event, I don't go into a panic wondering how I'll cope with it and stay in recovery. I know from practice and commitment that, one day at a time, I follow my personal plan of eating no matter what. The gift of recovery is that I love and prefer to stick to my plan. It gives me security and freedom from the disease mentality that goes with being wishy-washy about my plan of eating.

Recovery means that when the hard stuff of life comes my way, excess food and mental obsession are not options. Today I have the willingness to choose healthy ways to deal with difficult situations.

Being open with other people about my long-term recovery means they will watch me. That no longer scares me. If I honestly work my program, I'll carry a strong message about recovering from compulsive overeating and living a spiritual way of life.

—*New Zealand, June 2008*

Recovery Rocks!

I recently attended my retirement party. I'd been unhappy for a while but could not see a way out of being a wage slave. I prayed, and God sorted it out for me. Now I have an early retirement package and the chance to make a new start. I had a great time at the party, talked to new and old friends, didn't over-organize anything, and didn't agonize about things going wrong or people not turning up. I didn't do anything I'm ashamed of or need to apologize for. I remember how I acted and how I got into bed later that night. I didn't fall over, fall asleep, or fall face first into the buffet. All those things are miracles, and all are possible because of recovery. Recovery rocks!

The next morning, I woke up, thought back over my last day in the office, and remembered the party. I felt fine and smiled about how it had gone. I was staying in a hotel, so I showered, dressed, and set off for home. Outside, it was bright and sunny, cool and breezy. It felt good to be alive, awake, and walking. At the station a train was about to leave. I ran for it with my backpack on, and I didn't get out of breath or wheeze and cough. As I sat on the train, I thought, "Recovery rocks!"

I used to struggle to find clothes that looked good in my size. My largest pants had a 48-inch (122-cm) waist, and I wore baggy t-shirts with food stains. I had large shirts for the office that stretched across my belly. Today, I have some smart-looking shirts and cool t-shirts with no food stains. As I put on my 36-inch (91-cm) jeans, I'm not ashamed to see myself in the mirror. I think, "Wow! Recovery rocks!"

I used to think the world was unfair and spiteful. Why did such-and-such have to happen to me? Now I know I am blessed beyond words. My needs are taken care of when I leave it to God and stop trying to be God. I had always looked for the rulebook; others seemed to understand how to live, but I didn't. Now I have a wonderful and rewarding way of living. It's called recovery, and recovery rocks!

Sometimes stuff happens, because that's life. I could complain, fuss, shout, and scream. I could make it worse by indulging in my substance of choice to quell my fears. But just for today, I choose to trust in God, do my part, act as if, and look to see how I can help others.

Today I can choose recovery, because recovery rocks!

—*United Kingdom, July 2008*

The Recovery Path— Journey of Discovery

Recovery is like following a path through the countryside. Some paths appear to be a blind end, but when you get close to the end, something beautiful opens up before you. It is no good sitting in a car and looking out, thinking you are experiencing the beauties of the world. You must get out and walk one step at a time along the path. The path of recovery is the best thing I have ever done.

I came into OA in October 2003 and flung myself into the program. I had been suicidal and desperate to find a solution to my continuous bingeing. I have literally run along the path, not stopping to look at things. That doesn't work, but doing everything others have done before me gives good recovery.

The Steps have helped me look at my life and change. It is like being a butterfly emerging into a beautiful world. I had no idea recovery could feel so good, but I also feel that recovery is not a destination. I must always keep working on different parts of my life, and I will change as I grow older. I know I am one step away from returning to compulsive overeating, but I have made a thousand steps along the path of recovery.

If you have doubts about recovery, why not take those first baby steps and see how your life changes beyond your wildest dreams.

Today it is my choice to recover or not. I have all the tools and support to continue down that path. I don't want to return to sitting in the car looking out at the world. Recovery is much more than I could have dreamed.

—England, May 2005

I Chose Life

I come from a normal, functional family, although my parents are divorced. I have always been a high achiever and never had an eating problem growing up. However, when I started high school, I began to feel inferior and tried hard to get people to like and respect me. I became conscious of my figure and the figures of girls around me. I decided my stomach needed to be flatter, and a friend shared her diet. I stuck to a rigid routine of diet and exercise for six months, lost considerable weight, and stopped menstruating.

My parents and friends began to notice I was too thin. My parents took me to a dietician, who advised me to include certain foods in my diet. I did and gained 3 kg (7 lbs), which made me distressed and unhappy. My parents suggested I see a psychologist, who diagnosed me with anorexia. Anorexia made me feel in control and gave me a sense of power. It distinguished me from others and made me feel special in my diseased mind. It also got me the attention I craved, resulting in my unwillingness to get better. During a year of therapy, I became more ill and began purging when I ate a little more than I would have liked.

At the beginning of eleventh grade, I directed and produced a school play and became "too busy" to eat. My weight dropped to 35 kg (77 lbs), and my parents hospitalized me despite my numerous pleadings. Admitted just before my 17th birthday and petrified of gaining weight, I attempted to run away and was caught. Medical staff told me I would be locked up if I did not cooperate, but my father didn't want that, so he removed me from the hospital. We pleaded with my mother to take me back into her home, and she agreed on the grounds I come with her to work every day so she could make sure I was eating and refraining from purging.

In October while at my mother's work, I began bingeing. My inability to control my eating was my worst nightmare. Despite numerous attempts to stop, my bingeing got worse, and I began to gain weight. I became more depressed and struggled to complete my schoolwork because all I could do when I came home was eat. My mother would often get angry because I had eaten all the food in the house. She began locking the cupboards and freezer. But I still had access to food because I drove to supermarkets daily to buy binge foods. I isolated myself and refused to attend social gatherings because I was ashamed of the way I looked.

In August of my matriculation year, I had a minor car accident. At that moment I decided life was no longer worth living, so I overdosed on pills. My mother rushed me to the hospital, and the doctors pumped my stomach. While lying there, I realized I had to choose whether I wanted to live or die. Something told me I wanted to live, and my disease was standing in the way of my happiness. I became willing to do anything to get well.

My mother heard about Overeaters Anonymous through a colleague and believed OA might help me. As soon as the hospital discharged me, I attended my first OA meeting. What I found there was unlike anything I had ever seen before. Here were people who understood me and were willing to accept me no matter what. They told me I would recover from compulsive overeating, as long I was willing to work the program to the best of my ability and follow its suggestions. I learned I have a fatal disease, and while I am not to blame for having the disease, I am responsible for taking simple, daily actions to bring about my recovery.

The program does not just focus on my eating problems, but provides me with guidelines on how to cope with life without compulsive eating or starvation. It teaches me I have things to do just for today and I need to rely on a power greater than myself for direction. Through practicing the program and using its Tools, I have been able to refrain from bingeing and return to a healthy weight. I can now participate in life, instead of running away. I have a renewed enthusiasm and zest for life that I never thought I could have.

So many miraculous things are happening to me. I have many friends who accept and love me as I am, and I enjoy going out and socializing with them. I am in a wonderful, loving relationship and am even able to study a challenging degree at university. I no longer suffer continuous depression and embarrassment about who I am. I am grateful to this wonderful program for saving my life. I encourage anyone who has an eating disorder, be it anorexia, bulimia, or overeating, to try OA because it really works—if you work it!

—South Africa, February 2010

Finding Gratitude Everywhere

I came to OA fifteen months ago without much gratitude. I guess I had been taking everything for granted. As I worked the Steps, miracles started happening. People told me to pray, so I did, but I soon found I was thanking God for everything he gave me.

In the early days, I had to set a time to pray, but before long it came naturally. On tough days, I would pray all day, and my prayers were almost always to thank God.

My gratitude shone through when doctors diagnosed my dad with terminal cancer. Instead of throwing a pity party and saying "poor me," I prayed and thanked God for giving me this special time with Dad, since many people never get such an opportunity. As I wrote my annual Christmas letter, my husband told me, "I don't know why you even bother. We've had such a dreadful year, with one major problem after another." I did not see it that way. I had learned to turn my glass around and point out all the good things that had happened.

I had overcome major surgery, and I was still alive. My marriage had come close to divorce as I went through radical changes, but my husband had begun to see that our marriage would improve, and soon it was better than it had been in the last fourteen years. As for my dad's cancer, he was still here. We never know how many more days we have left together, but I know he will always be with me, and I am pleased he has witnessed me in recovery.

Miracles have happened. Today I have a new career I never imagined. Being blessed with all this gratitude has allowed me to leave the planning up to God. How wonderful my life is today.

—United Kingdom, September/October 2012

Revelation in India

I am 59 years old and have been a diabetic for sixteen years. After twenty-four years of sobriety, I couldn't understand why I wasn't able to control my weight or diabetes. I have done the Twelve Steps several times in another program, so I considered myself clean and in good spiritual condition.

In 2002, I took a friend's advice, bought OA literature, and shipped it to my home in India because OA had no real presence there. But I never opened the box! After six years, gaining many kilograms, visiting every slimming clinic in town, and still failing to relieve my overeating compulsion and weight gain, I became desperate.

My wife and I were cleaning the attic when she stumbled upon the unopened box of OA literature. She asked, "Why don't you try this anyway? After all, you've nothing but your weight to lose!" That was God's grace at work. I read all the OA literature as if my life depended on it, kicking myself for not doing so earlier!

When I spoke to a friend and found he, too, shared my problem, OA in Bangalore was born. But I am writing this because I made a near fatal mistake by thinking being a good practitioner of the AA Twelve Steps ought to have helped with my compulsive overeating! As our literature explains, while the Steps are the same, the way they work when I use them in OA is different. I was blind to how my emotional unmanageability led me to replace alcohol with food. I had not yet become obese, which delayed my acceptance of my compulsive eating.

I have seventy-five days of abstinence and have maintained a weight loss of 10 kilograms (23 lbs). My diabetes is under control. I feel more energetic, caring, and productive than I have felt in a decade! My group has grown from two to ten, giving each of us more strength to stay on the OA program. I am truly grateful to OA and the Fellowship for giving me a new lease on life!

—*India, December 2012*

Online Miracle

I am a compulsive eater in recovery. In February 2010, I went to my gynecologist and remarked that I was afraid of dying of cancer. She calmly told me that I should be afraid of dying of obesity. That same night, my 3-year-old daughter slept on the couch. I picked her up and started to cry, realizing that if I continued to eat as I was, I would not see my princess grow up. I wished deeply to stop eating that way and asked God for help.

To this day, remembering that moment moves me. Help came in a person who sent me an email talking about OA and the existence of OA online meetings here in Brazil. It is impossible to describe the happiness and relief I felt when I logged on to my first meeting and heard people talking about doing things I had done that made me feel deep shame. I had stolen food in the fridge belonging to others in the house, eaten sweets alone, broken endless promises to stop eating sugar, and tried to fill voids in my life with sugar. I had been careless with my body, not wanting to brush my teeth or shower.

I feel I was born again at that online meeting. Someone cared about me; I was not the problem I thought I was. (I'm crying while writing this because God was wonderful for leading me to the online meetings.) I spent the day attending these meetings, got a sponsor, and started giving service two months later to maintain those meetings that were saving my life. I think I was abstinent at that first meeting, when I felt hope that I could survive and stop eating that way. The online world was available to me every night in my house.

Since then, I have given service for maintenance of these online meetings that are an important part of my recovery. I share my joys, my troubles, and my hope to continue with the gift of abstinence I received from God at that first meeting. I participate in two or three online meetings each week, finding comrades in unconditional love. I am still working today with my fourth sponsor, who has been a blessing, and I serve on the National Service Board in Brazil. I also go to face-to-face meetings, but my home meetings have been online.

I have recovered physically, losing 42 kilograms (92 lbs) in the first two years. I have also recovered emotionally and spiritually. My continued abstinence is a blessing for someone who once set her sweet 3-year-old daughter aside to eat.

Only a miracle could make me stop my compulsive eating, and this miracle happened by the grace of God through the OA online meetings.

Grata.

—*Brazil, May 2013*

Abstinence Tastes Better!

When I joined OA, I was obese, defeated, desperate, and unhappy. I weighed 93 kilograms (205 lbs) at 156 cm (5 feet 1 inch) tall. I was suffering from a fatty liver, reflux, shortness of breath on exertion, exhaustion, and postnatal depression. I had a victim mentality and thought the universe had conspired to make my life difficult. And I was married and could not provide for the needs of my three small children.

At my first Overeaters Anonymous meeting, I felt accepted and welcomed. Initially I just went to the meetings and continued to eat the way I always had. That first year, I went to the Queensland, Australia, OA convention. Afterwards I was able stay with three meals a day and nothing in between for six months, losing six kilograms (13 lbs). Then things began to slip. I became disenchanted and left OA to continue my familiar roundabout of dieting and bingeing.

A few years later, I rejoined OA. Weighing 97 kilograms (214 lbs) and being more unwell than ever, I began working the program in earnest. I opened the *Twelve and Twelve* (*The Twelve Steps and Twelve Traditions of Overeaters Anonymous*) I had bought years earlier and began the Steps. I attended meetings, got a sponsor, and started writing, making phone calls, and reading OA literature.

After reading the OA pamphlet *A Plan of Eating*, I removed suspected trigger foods from my diet and avoided situations that could lead to overeating, but I had no idea what a normal amount of food was. Next I found the pamphlet *Dignity of Choice*, and I chose an eating plan and started weighing my food. I still binged on occasion, but my binges were not as bad as before.

I was lucky to attend a luncheon where a fellow OA member said she had benefited from removing dairy products from her diet. I remained silent and refused to listen to what she said, but she had planted a seed. I had already removed wheat and sugar from my diet, so maybe dairy was also a trigger food. With reluctance, I removed dairy products from my food for two days, but being a strong-willed person who was unwilling to go without them, I reintroduced dairy products to see if that would be okay. Silly me! This resulted in three days of bingeing as if there were no tomorrow.

Having learned my lesson the hard way, I ceased eating dairy products. The change in me is amazing! I am clear-headed and energetic. The severe hunger pains, which plagued me all my life, are gone. I am down to 72 kilograms (159 lbs) and still dropping.

Recently my doctor informed me I no longer have a fatty liver. I am working the Steps, and I have a good relationship with my Higher Power, husband, and children. My goal in life is to find balance and just be me. I love my life and the people in it. The promises of the program are true and will be fulfilled if you are willing to follow the program and go to any lengths to achieve abstinence. Abstinence tastes far better than any dairy product ever could!

—*Australia, November 2013*

LONG-TERM RECOVERY

This Girl's Tale

Seventeen years ago, this girl walked into her first OA meeting. She had reached 248 pounds (112 kg) some time back, and the solution was to stop weighing herself. Unfortunately, that didn't stop her uncontrolled binges, and she went up another dress size. She had considered taking her own life, but then a friend took her to an OA meeting.

She scanned the tables for "the diet" but found none. The concepts were foreign—get a sponsor, take the Steps, and call three people a day. None of the sponsors were available, so what could she do? But, for the first time in a long time, she had hope. OA was not like diet clubs. Most of the OA women had normal body sizes. Some were fat like her, but even what they shared sounded hopeful!

At the end of the meeting, they gave out poker chips for abstinent people. What did "abstinent" mean? She knew she must have one of those white chips because she was tired of her life. She wanted to be a member of this club.

The following night she went to another OA meeting. This time a woman said she was a sponsor and did not say she was unavailable. After the meeting she asked the woman to be her sponsor. The woman agreed and told her to call the next day and not eat any sugar. Bizarre as it was, she did it, and life as she knew it was over.

With her sponsor, she jumped into the Steps. She thought she'd try the Twelve Step, twelve-week plan, graduate, and never be fat again. So each week she talked to her sponsor about a Step. By the fifth week, she was on Step Five, losing weight at a good clip, and answering all the questions from *The Twelve Steps of Overeaters Anonymous* (the Traditions part had not yet been written).

Over time she learned it doesn't work that way. We don't

graduate. It is a lifelong process, one day at a time. "Whatever," she thought, but still did everything her sponsor suggested.

As time went on, 100-plus pounds (45-kg) of excess weight melted away. She understood more about how OA works because her life felt so much better than before. She'd arrive early at meetings, help put out chairs, and talk to newcomers. A girl at the meeting got a ninety day abstinence coin. Wow! If that girl could do it, so could she!

Today, she still goes to OA meetings and has a normal body size. She has had several different sponsors over the years. She has taken the Steps several times over, and her food plan has changed many times. Now when they ask for sponsors, she always raises her hand. She has been chairwoman of an OA region and knows that doesn't make her important. She is just another bozo on the bus, and giving back is important.

She loves her life again, and people love her. Unlike those diet clubs, OA helped her understand why she ate like that. When she reached a normal body size, she didn't have to celebrate at a doughnut shop. No, she quietly wrote this story, hoping it would help another compulsive overeater who still suffers. She puts her abstinence first, absolutely. Today she cares about others.

I celebrate my abstinence through God's grace and your help! I am grateful to all who've walked this path with me. I'm no longer a woman who abuses food. I like who I am today—can you believe it? I think I'll keep coming back.

—June 2012

Standouts

I'm grateful for my years of abstinence, which started at my second OA meeting in December 1980. I'm grateful to a small woman who approached me, asked if I had a sponsor, and offered to take my call the next morning at 6 a.m. At age 25, I hardly knew 6 a.m. existed, but I did call, and I kept calling. She helped me realize many things, and the following stand out:

- Abstinence, which results in physical recovery, is the most important thing in my life without exception. It comes before my relationship with my Higher Power, which would vanish if I went back to the food; my relationships with my family, which would implode; my job, which I would probably lose; and my religion, which would be meaningless.

- Abstinence—being abstinent and staying abstinent—is the greatest service I can do for OA. If I am in the food, then organizing share-a-thons, taking and making calls to newcomers, or speaking at meetings would be merely self-serving and not genuine service to the Fellowship. It could even be harmful to OA as a whole. Being abstinent today shows people the program works. My sponsor told me if I were to relapse, I would have to give up my OA responsibilities, sit down, shut my mouth, and open my ears. She assured me I would have nothing to share if I were not abstinent; I would be as good as drunk. I could still do service by setting out chairs and cleaning up.

- Abstinence does not have to lead to relapse. Recovery is possible in this program just as it is in other Twelve Step programs. My first sponsor led me through the first nine Steps, an eighteen-month process for me. She expected me to take action on whatever Step I was working on that day and did not let me proceed until I had convinced both of us that I had worked a Step thoroughly and without reservation.

- Having taken a thorough Step One, I've never had to reconsider if I am a compulsive overeater. I've never had to wonder if my life would be unmanageable if I returned to the food. Having taken a thorough Step Two, I have never had to wonder if there's a way out, a way back to sanity. Having taken a thorough Step Three twenty-seven years ago, I have never had to take back the solo controls for my life, which never worked anyway. I still believe if I work the Step I'm on today (Steps Ten, Eleven, and Twelve), I will not go back to the food. How could I, since each day I turn my will and life over to the care of my Higher Power?

- Abstinence is an act of surrender, not control. Eating right was a new concept for me, and letting go of weight control scared me. But I did let go, and I'm so glad! By working the Twelve Steps and living with a desire not to overeat today, I have maintained my weight loss of 30 pounds (14 kg) and have done so (except for two pregnancies) for more than twenty-six years. Since I completed Step Nine twenty-six years ago, sanity has become my way of life—not always easy, but always worth it.

I am grateful for my physical, emotional, and spiritual recovery. I am grateful for the opportunities I have to share this amazing program with others. I am grateful for the Steps and my commitment to work the Step I am on today. I am grateful to my Higher Power, who is always within reach, even when I can't sense it. And I am grateful for my first sponsor, who showed me this simple path of recovery out of the food and onto a new plane of existence.

—August 2008

Recovery Insurance

When exploring my OA region's website, I found a link to a locally produced–literature document called the *Recovery Insurance Policy**. It is an agreement between two or more OA members to take specific actions if one of the signing parties shows signs of compulsive eating.

What a wonderful, loving, concrete way to put into action the communal "we" partnership of our program! It reinforces the idea we are not meant to do this alone: "The amazing secret to the success of this program is just that: weakness. It is weakness, not strength, that binds us to each other and to a higher power and somehow gives us the ability to do what we cannot do alone" (*Overeaters Anonymous,* 3rd ed., p. 4).

The *Recovery Insurance Policy* reminds me of a personal relapse prevention plan my sponsor had me write several years ago when I was struggling with relapse. Over the last several weeks, that plan has worked! Surprise, surprise: the plan involves the Tools and Steps! The more I work the Tools and Steps, the more recovery and abstinence I gain and the more joy, honesty, clarity, love, and compassion I give myself, my Higher Power, and the beings with whom I share this earth.

When strong cravings hit, here are some strategies in my personal relapse prevention plan:

- I commit to waiting five minutes. In those five minutes, I say the first three Steps and pray for the willingness to hear Higher Power's alternatives to hurting myself.
- I commit to calling my sponsor. If I can't get him or her, I leave a message, being honest about the cravings and

---

*The *Recovery Insurance Policy* can be found in the *Twelfth Step Within Handbook* and at oa.org under "Twelfth Step Within."

aware of why they've surfaced, such as maybe I had a fight with my mom. Then I make another call.

- I pick up a Tool like literature and keep it where I can't avoid it: my purse, car, powder room, or kitchen. My sponsor had me post signs in my house with program slogans and "God loves you; you don't need to eat" on them. Most guests understand.

- I visit the OA website (oa.org) and listen to a podcast if it's too late to call anyone.

- I remember I'm not alone. I let someone else in program be my Higher Power with flesh—in person, on the phone, on paper, or on the Web.

- I remember what I feel when I wake up after a binge: shame, self-anger, regret, sorrow, distance from God, irritabe, and self-pity. Then I remember how I feel when I am constructive in enduring hard feelings: ready to be of service to others, humble yet prideful, close to God, clear-headed, loved, confident, and trusting of the program and my fellows.

- I do service even when I feel least like doing it, when self-pity and anger make me feel like the world owes me. Even the smallest kind of service works, including writing a paragraph for an OA newsletter; leaving a message for someone; showing up to a phone, face-to-face, or online meeting; or sending a card or email to a non-OA friend.

- I pray for those with whom I am angry, even if I have to act as if. I keep a list of nonaddictive, fun, comforting or challenging treats: listening to music, cuddling with my pet, watching funny or uplifting films, reading books, swimming, walking, buying flowers, drinking tea, chewing sugarless gum, visiting educational or entertaining websites, drumming, making a gratitude list, doing gentle stretching exercises, talking with a friend, and taking a hot bath or shower.

These strategies help fulfill the needs I'm trying to satisfy with food, without hurting myself. Humor and community are powerful weapons in my arsenal against my disease, especially if I can share with someone!

—May 2010

Huntington Men's Meeting, 1979

About a year ago, a group of men with varying lengths of time in Overeaters Anonymous met in a member's home to explore the feasibility of forming a men's group. These men felt that while it was important to continue to attend other OA meetings, a special need existed for a place where men could share feelings many were unable to express elsewhere. That was how the Wednesday night men's group of Huntington, New York USA began.

Many men have come to the meeting and some have gone; men from all walks of life—truck drivers, businessmen, teachers, retirees—have been getting together every Wednesday to share and explore how the OA program is helping them achieve recovery from compulsive overeating.

Here, a truck driver can shed a tear and talk about the difficulties he's having with his family and about how he is able to gather strength to deal with his problems by working the program. On this one night of the week, we are with the man who goes to a business dinner and can't fit into the chair at the table.

We take this beautiful program one day at a time and look forward to celebrating many more anniversaries of the Wednesday night men's meeting of Overeaters Anonymous.

—February 1981

Huntington Men's Meeting, Today

I am a man who has been in program thirty-three years and never stopped attending meetings. I have overcome many character defects, but procrastination still plagues me.

In 1981, *Lifeline* published an article I wrote about the first year anniversary of the men's Huntington, New York OA meeting. I have procrastinated until now to submit another story.

Our meeting has met continually since 1979. We celebrated the start of our thirtieth year in 2009 in the same meeting place. Our numbers have dwindled, but we have more than enough participants to keep going.

At our meetings, men can be open and honest, sharing their feelings without judgment. The impact of these emotions plays an integral role in our recovery. Some participants have left and others passed on, yet each week, support is strong and sharing is real, a cornerstone of our recovery program.

The men are at various levels of recovery. One constant remains: the desire to stop eating compulsively. We've heard thousands of tales, and we accept all without judgment. Here, men can abandon the need to create a macho image and can be human, with both strengths and weaknesses.

I have been able to maintain a weight loss of 55 pounds (25 kg) with the program's support. More important, I have stopped eating compulsively.

We look forward to more meetings and invite men (women have also attended with a warm welcome) to join us at our Huntington, New York meetings on Wednesdays at 7:30 p.m.

—*May 2010*

An Okay Mom

Last week my baby turned 1 year old. This special event was even more special because of my recovery. I had my last binge when I was five months pregnant. Thanks to the grace of God and the support of this amazing program, I have not picked up the food since then.

My greatest fear when I found out I was pregnant was the thought of being at home with nothing to stop me from going on all-out, all-day binges. I wouldn't have the pressure of time limitations, deadlines, and fitting into corporate clothes to curb my eating. I knew I could easily become a negligent mother if I was into the food. I knew this disease would lead me to leaving my baby alone in the house while I went out to get my binge foods. I knew I wouldn't really be there even when I was with him. Thoughts of the next binge or remorse from the last one would preoccupy me.

The power of this program means that when I look back on the last year, I would not change a thing about my mothering. I really have been present with my son, even during those tricky days of tiredness, sickness, and soul-searching about being a stay-at-home mother. I've experienced many moments of joy, as I have learned how to be a child again while still being a responsible adult. I know that the only perfect parent is God. If I call on him for guidance, I can be an okay mom, and being an okay mom is okay with me today. I can relax and go with the flow. This is major progress for me because I default to perfectionism under pressure.

When I look at my baby, I remember that I am looking after two babies, my son and my recovery. Both need tender nurturing every day to continue growing strong. I know this is a one-day-at-a-time solution, but I also know that God promises me permanent recovery if I continue to do the things each day that have kept me well so far.

As it says in the Big Book, "The very simple program they advised me to follow was that I should ask to know God's will for me for that one day, and then, to the best of my ability, to follow that, and at night to express my gratefulness to God for the things that had happened to me during the day" (*Alcoholics Anonymous*, 3rd ed., pp 208-209).

This simplicity is the real joy and power of this program.

—*September 2005*

Farewell to Fear

I thought I was a wonderful plump lady with no problems other than being a little chubby. Okay, so I did feel guilty when I drove around eating day-old baked goods, taking care to stay out of my neighborhood, and searching for isolated dumpsters to dispose of the evidence. And I guess most people when buying bags of sweets don't invent stories for the cashier about being the candy lady at work. And most wives don't pick up fast food for a family of four, food that never makes it home, and then eat again after making dinner for just herself and her husband because the fast food went down so fast!

At 250 pounds (113 kg), I was in much denial. Food anesthetized me. It took about a year in OA to take off 125 pounds (57 kg) with the help of a sponsor and food plan that eliminated my binge foods. My head cleared. Attending meetings, using a sponsor, and working the Steps helped me see I had more work to do. It has been scary and overwhelming at times, but the Fellowship has supported me to look at the truth, ask for direction and help, and make changes.

So what has changed?

Obviously my size has changed, but so has my feeling about looking at myself in the mirror. I can look at my whole self naked, not just my face. My doctor says I'm in great shape for a 65-year-old woman, and my husband of forty-four years agrees! Now when my doctor asks me to take medication, I take it as prescribed instead of what seems right to me. By following my sponsor's suggestion of weighing only once a month, I have been freed of my obsession with the scale. I have guilt-free eating, and I don't crave. When my meal is over, I feel full and content. I have never felt that way before, no matter how much binge food I ate. I don't worry about what people think of my special orders at restaurants. I am happy about how I look. Wahoo!

Fear used to drive my life. Today, I recognize that my perfectionism and desire to control are manifestations of fear. Pride, self-sufficiency, competitiveness, and self-righteousness were cover-ups for low self-esteem. Higher Power graces me with honesty about my flaws, willingness to work the Steps, and an open mind to set aside what I think I know, for a new experience of recovery when I am spiritually fit.

Sounds grand, doesn't it? Well, it's a darned good thing Steps Ten and Eleven are part of my program. Sometimes my honesty is nudged when a friend says, "Ouch, that hurt!" It gives me an opportunity to take a rigorous look at my actions. I ask daily for help from Higher Power because I need it: help to stay abstinent, help to be a kind and loving person, and help to remember my Third Step commitment. I still have plenty of work to do, but I am so much better than I was.

Today my action plan includes successful habits like making a meal plan for the day ahead, asking for help from my Higher Power and sponsor, reading OA and AA literature, spending quiet time with my Higher Power, communicating with other OA members about recovery, attending many meetings, not eating when I'm angry, organizing my day, not doing "one last thing," keeping the bed made and the laundry done, being nice to my husband, and thanking Higher Power for the day. I try to keep an open heart and treat others as I would like to be treated. I try to have a flexible mind to let new ideas in and keep thoughts that don't serve me out. I am working on decluttering my closets and life. I have a sense of social obligation. I am a poll worker during elections, volunteer at a performing arts center, helper at a church, and food collector for a local food bank. Recovery has reordered my priorities.

My world is fuller because of the spiritual awakening I received as a recovery gift in OA and because of my seven-plus years of abstinence. My Higher Power is crazy about me. When the fears return, the fear prayer my sponsor taught me always makes me feel better:

—June 2012

One Bite Away

I keep coming back because I do not ever want to return to the mental torture, shame, and physical pain of compulsive overeating. Thanks to the honesty learned in this program, I know that OA is the only thing that has ever worked for me long-term.

I keep coming back thanks to my Higher Power, whom I choose to call God and without whom none of this would be possible. I have been blessed with the gift of desperation. I am convinced to my innermost core that I will always be just one bite away from my worst binge ever.

No matter how long I have been abstinent, I will never be cured, I will never "have it made," and I will always be at day one.

If I go too long without working my program disciplines and the Tools, I begin to get cravings. However, this program gives me a guaranteed way to keep the cravings down: practice the OA Principles in all my affairs and work the Tools by going to meetings, calling my sponsor and other OA members, maintaining a plan of eating, doing program readings and writings, giving service, practicing anonymity, and having an action plan.

I try to keep my memory green through sharing my story and working with other compulsive overeaters. Only God's grace gave me the willingness to do any of these disciplines. It is the only reason I have been able to maintain my abstinence one day at a time, one meal at a time, or even one minute at a time; I have been free of sugar, wheat, and flour since December 1999.

I keep coming back because with program I have a life beyond my wildest dreams. Thank you, God; thank you, OA!

—August 2013

Working the Steps Works

The Twelve Steps work if I work them. Eight years ago, after twelve years of sporadic abstinence in Overeaters Anonymous, I finally hit a bottom that hurt enough to motivate me to get a food plan, stick to it, and start working the Twelve Steps in order. That didn't leave much time in my day for bingeing.

I practiced Step One by following a disciplined plan of eating, abstaining from sugar and refined carbohydrates, attending meetings, and using all the program Tools. Doing these things meant I was practicing Step Two, because I was believing in a power greater than myself. In this case, the power was the OA program and specifically Step Three.

After thirty days of abstinence, I began my Fourth Step. I answered specific questions about my life, from childhood to adulthood, writing for twenty minutes every morning before going to work.

I did my Fifth Step with a sponsor. Nothing spectacular happened when I finished it; I just felt relieved it was finished. Steps Six and Seven weren't too difficult. I did them immediately after I finished my Fifth Step.

I did my Eighth Step by listing the people I wrote about in my Fourth Step. Then, one by one, I made amends to those people. Before each amends, I discussed my approach with my sponsor, who is an OA longtimer. That was important because my aim was to try to amend the relationship, not to offend the person to whom I was apologizing.

Step Ten, in my understanding, is to rectify errors I make in daily life. Once I realize I may have offended someone or spoken out of turn, I try to amend that situation. While I was eating, I burned many bridges. The Twelve Steps are about building bridges.

I practice Step Eleven by not cramming too many activities into my day. This gives me time to "stop and smell the roses," and it has helped slow my thinking process. I enjoy needlework, and this is another form of meditation.

Step Twelve is about giving service by helping to carry the message of recovery to another compulsive overeater. Twelfth Step work in OA isn't only confined to recruiting newcomers. Many people already in our rooms also need a hand.

I hope I don't give the impression of having a flawless program or personality. Though I have not binged since November 1994, my program is far from perfect. I am continually refining and defining myself.

—August 2013

Reclaiming My Life

I walked into the OA rooms more than fourteen years ago weighing 90 pounds (41 kg), seeking a cure for my bingeing but completely denying my anorexia and exercise bulimia. The food plan most often discussed in meetings involved no sugar or white flour. This plan worked for me initially, and I rapidly (if superficially) completed the first four Steps with a sponsor. However, soon I began bingeing more than ever, a situation made worse by a move out of state.

Frustrated and frightened by my compulsive eating and with exercise no longer sufficient to keep off the pounds, I found a new sponsor and began to commit my food daily. However, I could not achieve more than a few weeks of abstinence and constantly fought painful cravings. After each binge, I would try a different food plan, cutting out more foods that I thought were triggering my overeating. Yet my bingeing episodes only grew worse. Frantic for the fix, I began to use vomiting, which quickly took over my life. It made me feel more insane since it enabled me to consume even greater quantities of food. I continued to gain weight until I weighed 60 pounds (27 kg) more than when I first entered OA, all the while attending meetings and working the Steps.

I moved again for job reasons and found anorexic/bulimic–focus meetings in my new city. Listening for the first time to the stories of anorexics and bulimics, I conceded my food problem involved more than compulsive overeating. While I hated bingeing and was quick to admit in OA I was powerless over it, I was loath to acknowledge my powerlessness over my eating behavior, compulsive exercising, and vomiting. I had not wanted to give them up until the bingeing stopped, rationalizing I was never skinny enough and did not vomit enough to qualify as anorexic or bulimic. Recovering members helped me realize that only by stopping the purging and restrictive behavior could I find freedom from bingeing.

I began to cobble together a semblance of abstinence. I stopped borrowing other people's food plans and created one specific to my food compulsions. More important, I let go of the diet mentality. Before, I knew only perfect bingeing or perfect eating. Now I put shades of gray into my abstinence. Adding sugar and white flour to my diet was scary, but I slowly understood that the more I labeled a food off-limits, the more I tended to binge on it. I also had to face a tremendous fear of fats. I cried the first time I ate, within my abstinence, a burrito with cheese. Equally scary after a binge was forgiving myself and sitting with that awful feeling of fullness instead of throwing up, over-exercising, or semi-starving myself.

Finally, I turned my weight over to God. For the first time, I wanted to be sane more than to be thin. With a new acceptance of my disease and powerlessness over it, I continued to work the Steps with a sponsor.

With this new approach, I did not achieve long-term abstinence instantly, but over time, the periods between binges grew longer and my food and weight obsessions subsided. I lost 40 of the pounds (18 kg) I had gained after entering program and reached a healthy and comfortable weight.

Today, I can say with gratitude that I am free of my obsession. I have maintained this abstinence through several moves, frequent foreign travel, marriage, and pregnancy. In each new city where I've lived, I've helped form an anorexic/bulimic–focus meeting. This allows me to have a place where I can find others with my specific food issues and to be there for OA members who need help with this angle of the disease.

—*March 2006*

11

GRATITUDE

Gratitude—the Attitude to Have

Gratitude has been the cornerstone of my OA recovery program for nearly fifteen years. "November is gratitude month" is something I heard in my early program days and have seldom heard since. Gratitude was a foreign concept to me. Complaining and whining—that I understood.

I brought forty years of negative thinking to the table. The first time I sat down with a piece of blank paper to write down one thing I was grateful for, I was stumped. Conversely, I could have filled the page with resentments, problems, and obstacles in my day. I sat for a long time with my blank piece of paper until I finally came up with one thing: dry roads for my forty-five-minute commute. Cultivating an attitude of gratitude is a skill that can be learned. Practicing gratitude taught me I did not have a bad day; I had a difficult moment, phone call, or meeting. A tense conversation, for example, might be ten minutes out of a twenty-four hour day.

Since I entered Overeaters Anonymous in 1989, I have had many challenges in my life: skin cancer, two moves, separation and divorce, an empty nest, organizational changes at work, loss of friendships, family estrangement, remarriage, the death of my only child, a misdiagnosed injury, and a broken foot with twelve weeks in a cast. Each of these situations held multiple opportunities for gratitude. When I am in physical or emotional pain, my antidote is to reach out and find something to be thankful for. After a decade of practice writing out my gratitude list, I often have an automatic response. Now, in a crisis, I can call up a mental or verbal list.

I still write out my list most of the time. Whenever I feel "restless, irritable and discontented," as the Big Book says (*Alcoholics Anonymous,* 4th ed., p. xxviii), I find paper and start writing a list. When I finish, I feel calmer and more grounded.

My attitude tilts in a positive direction.

Recently I was flipping through an old journal. To my surprise, I wrote a full gratitude list two days after my daughter's unexpected death. I do not remember doing this, but it was my handwriting and the things I wrote still ring true today:

- Family Medical Leave Act
- My husband
- Daylight and warmth (June)
- My friend S.
- My daughter's birth

When faced with a problem of any magnitude, my first question is, "What's good about this?" Practicing gratitude is an instant mood elevator because it puts the focus on abundance rather than lack. My glass is not half full—it is overflowing.

—August 2005

Singing with Gratitude

At meetings, I introduce myself as "a grateful, recovering compulsive overeater and a beautiful child of a loving God. Because of the grace of God and the help of people in this program, I am over 100 pounds (45 kg) lighter than I was at my top weight of 305 pounds (138 kg), and I am truly grateful."

I have found that the secret to inner joy is gratitude for everything God has given me, including the fact that he made me a compulsive overeater. I truly believe the reason I weighed 260 pounds (118 kg) at the age of 21, when I found OA, and survived several relapses over the twenty-six years I've been in the program is so I can help others. What a joy! Of course I am grateful for my recovery, but I find it spiritually rewarding to help guide others along the path of the Twelve Steps and see them blossom into the beautiful people God intended them to be. Last week, I was angry with God because my mother was dying of brain cancer, and I was not in a relationship I wanted. Basically, I was not getting my way in life. I also felt sad and depressed. I'd been angry for over two weeks and was taking it out on people around me.

At a meeting, a former sponsor suggested I go alone to a safe place and just yell at God and tell him how mad I was at him. I went to the chapel in the building, followed instructions, and then sat and cried for a minute. Soon I had the awesome feeling that God was taking care of me. He had provided competent and reliable caregivers in my parents' home, so I did not have to provide hands-on care. He was keeping me out of relationships that could harm me. He was providing generous support for my financial needs. Most of all, he has given me wonderful OA friends I can count on, miraculous recovery, and an incredible spiritual way of life in the Twelve Steps.

A few days later, my sponsor had me write a gratitude list. Joy that made me want to sing had replaced the self-pity, resentment, and depression! It welled up from deep inside me and made me want to share this program with anyone who would listen.

Joy does not depend on circumstances. It is a gift, an attitude change, always available to us through our Higher Power when we are willing to be grateful.

—*September/October 2009*

Letting Go

I cannot adequately describe the relief and gratitude I feel for being released from compulsive overeating.

When I came into OA, I could not stop thinking about my body, next diet, and food. I could not stop bingeing. In my early 20s, a doctor told me that if I continued to eat the way I was, I would be in a wheelchair by the time I was 40. I looked at him and said, "That does not help me because *I cannot stop.* It just makes me hate myself more to know I'm killing myself."

My obsession would not loosen its grip for even fifteen minutes.

I recently celebrated fifteen years of abstinence. The gap between fifteen minutes of hanging on and fifteen years of peaceful abstinence came through the slogan "let go and let God." Let go and let God captures the essence of the Twelve Steps. The Big Book says, "Some of us have tried to hold on to our old ideas and the result was nil until we let go absolutely" (*Alcoholics Anonymous*, 4th ed., p. 58).

At the beginning, I had to let go of two things simultaneously: my binge foods and my concept of God.

As soon as I adopted a plan of eating, I needed to find a power greater than myself that could enable me to adhere to it. I temporarily set aside my old idea of God and wrote out a new one—a God that could get me through the day without breaking my abstinence.

My new concept of God was of a power that delighted in me and at a moment's notice could usher in an army of angels to stand between my binge foods and me. This power wanted me to have a gorgeous life and could take away my desire to eat compulsively. Then I acted as if this power were real. Every time I was tempted, I would call on this power. Every time, it would come and do for me what I could not do for myself.

When I am afraid to let go and let God, I have to look at my concept of God. If I reconnect with the idea of a loving God that wants me to have a beautiful life, then letting go is much easier.

Letting go of the food and my old concept of a punishing God was just a beginning. My complete release from food obsession has also required that I let go of self-centeredness, resentment, and fears. In the morning, I ask God to enable me to let go of self-will and be a channel of service. I don't do this perfectly—not even close—but the willingness is enough. In exchange, I have experienced complete release from bingeing and food obsession, one day at a time, for over fifteen years.

—May 2009

Grateful for a Slogan

Keep coming back" is one of the most important slogans for my recovery. I am now abstinent, and I am happier and healthier than I have ever been. I have a 70-pound (32-kg) weight loss and seventeen months of abstinence because I kept coming back to OA.

It's important to keep coming back because real change is a slow process, one that is hard to measure. After a year in program, I told my sponsor I felt frustrated because I hadn't changed at all. She told me I had changed but was too close to my own situation to see it. I trusted my sponsor and the program, so I kept coming back to OA.

Sometimes it's hard to be patient, but I'm glad I was. I slowly began to see that I was changing. After two years in the program, I felt saner, happier, and more useful. All the small changes were slowly adding up, and I could see I was becoming a different person—the person God had designed me to be.

While it felt wonderful to feel serenity and faith grow inside me, I continued to struggle with the food. I knew I would never quit OA, but sometimes it got awfully hard. I watched others in my group achieve abstinence soon after arriving in the rooms, while I struggled for three years and couldn't seem to put the food down.

I often felt I would never get abstinent and was sometimes filled with despair, but I kept coming back to OA and working the program. God gave me an instinctive knowledge that OA was the only place I could find recovery and peace. Finally, after three years, I became abstinent—and the number one contributing factor is that I never gave up. I kept coming back.

Some people get abstinent right away, but a lot of people don't. I've seen many people get discouraged and leave after a year or two because they were struggling to become abstinent. I'm grateful I never left OA. Nothing else is out there that can help me, and I'm sure if I had left, I would never have found what I have now.

I'm grateful that I kept coming back until I got abstinent. I'm grateful for the slogan "Keep coming back until the miracle happens for you."

—May 2009

Vein of Gold

I picture recovery a lot like a vein of gold in a mine. Before the gold can be discovered, the miners have to pick and dig around to uncover it. Once the gold is uncovered, the miners follow the vein because, in general, where a nugget is found, more will follow.

Recovery has been like that. OA has given me the gift of recovery and many wonderful discoveries because I've worked at digging and unearthing what lies beneath the surface of my addiction. My sponsor and therapist were gentle when suggesting I work on developing my spiritual program and connection with a Higher Power. This work has brought forth a deepening recovery.

Some of the actions I've taken to help me grow and unearth these gifts are:

- praying first thing in the morning to ask for help and last thing at night to say thank you;
- meditating and journaling, by writing my thoughts, asking for help, and listening for guidance;
- attending retreats and listening to others share their spiritual development, experience, strength, and hope in recovery; and
- working the Steps: Step Two to develop a concept of a Higher Power, Step Three to connect with Higher Power, Step Four to clean house and lift away the earth, and Step Nine to sweep clean the messes I've made and open the pathway to healing and growth.

What are some of the gold nuggets I've discovered? They are:

- wearing the same-sized clothes now for ten to twelve years;
- going to graduate school, graduating, and loving what I do

as a result;

- developing a healthy, honest, loving relationship with my spouse and partner;
- watching my sponsees grow and learn about themselves while in recovery;
- making amends and gaining a friend out of that process;
- finding unconditional acceptance from my sponsor after being honest and truthful;
- getting full before I finish all the food on my plate;
- maintaining a 40-pound (18-kg) weight loss (give or take a few pounds) over the last ten to twelve years;
- receiving a coin for fourteen years of abstinence (I have never done anything for fourteen years!); and
- facing one of my biggest fears, going through it, and living to tell about it.

Thank you, OA, for a sparkling, valuable, and wonderful life through recovery. Life is all golden in abstinence!

—*January 2010*

Group Power

At the meeting where my group celebrated its thirtieth birthday, I got so choked up I couldn't speak. I tried after the meeting, but words wouldn't come.

The next day, I sent an email to my sponsor and others explaining what I had tried to say. My sponsor said I should forward the email to *Lifeline*; I always try to do what my sponsor says! Here is the email.

"Well, that was embarrassing! I don't know what happened last night. I just wanted to share what this meeting has meant to me. I haven't had such trouble sharing in a long time. Anyway, I am just going to keep coming back! So there! Since I couldn't say what I wanted to, I am going to try today.

"This meeting is the first I ever attended, and it saved my life. I mean it! Maybe I couldn't share because I thought about it too much.

"When I came to my first meeting, I was at the end of my rope. It was the last attempt to get my life back under control. No chairs were available when I walked in, but a woman went in the hall and got me one! She didn't look at me with disgust. I could tell she wanted me there. I had never felt so welcome!

"I remember several members' shares. While our stories were nothing alike, it was obvious they also had a problem with food. I had never heard anyone be so honest about something like that. It touched my heart.

"We used to take a fifteen minute break during the meeting, and a member would take newcomers to another room and teach them about the program before they returned to the regular meeting. The man who led the newcomers at my first meeting became my sponsor. He spoke about a man present who had lost over 100 pounds (45 kg)! Although I was 250 pounds (113 kg) overweight, it gave me hope. That first night was life changing.

"Of course, the old me still tried to come through. After a few meetings, my stinking thinking resumed. How could they want *me*? After my fourth meeting, a member followed me into the parking lot and asked me to be group treasurer. *Me*? I was never more happy and thrilled to be asked to do something! It meant she wanted and needed me there. I wasn't just someone they tolerated. I belonged—imagine that! Just being tolerated in other organizations had been the norm for me; my self-worth could not have been lower.

"My meeting—the wonderful people who are that meeting—gave me purpose. The OA program has taught me so much! Even in relapse I have been grateful for my group and the Big Book.

"This is what I wanted to say last night. I'm not giving up! My fellow group members will just have to put up with my bawling like a baby, because I can't quit coming and trying to share. I don't have an option, and I don't want one!

"It's a tribute to the power of meetings, service, and making newcomers feel at home that I now weigh 196 pounds (89 kg) instead of 450 pounds (204 kg). Thanks, McKinney Care and Share!"

—December 2010

Member of Society

When I dwell on how bad my life is, how hard and cruel this world is, and how most people are against me, I cannot see the forest for the trees. I cannot see the truths that people are good and my life is so much better than it was when I was caught up in practicing my disease. When my mind is full of negative thoughts, it's too easy to forget that many people have more difficult lives than I do and that God has changed me from a selfish, self-centered person into a kind, loving, caring human being. Now, I am a member of society instead of the center of the universe.

God also enables me to handle any situation without having to compulsively overeat. For a person who used to wake every day knowing he was powerless over food and would destroy his physical, emotional, and spiritual self, hating himself for it, I now find the difference in my quality of life is almost unfathomable. Someone like me, who thought only of himself and what he could get out of life, is now someone who wants to help others and be the best person he can be. This is a gift of grace from God.

I am grateful today for my family, health, job, home, and most of all, the Fellowship of Overeaters Anonymous and the release from the compulsion to overeat. Even if these gifts were all life had to offer, they would be enough to keep me happy, joyous, and free for the rest of my life, one day at a time.

—September/October 2012

If You Work It

To this day, I have been blessed with continuous abstinence. I joined the OA program in September 2004, and my commitment to abstinence began in October of that year. It took me a good four weeks of crash-and-burn incidences with food to recognize I am not normal around food, nor shall I ever be. What a liberation this admission is in my life, for today.

I have just returned home from a short holiday spent in a quiet beach house. Telephone reception was limited; and being blessed with daily phone calls from sponsees and a daily call to my sponsor, I was nervous about this break in routine. I'm thankful a wise member in program reminded me I must pick up the OA Tools that are available in any given circumstance—and not just pick them up, but *use* them.

Now back home and having enjoyed several abstinent days away, I realize that this inspired program truly does work if we work it. The details of how we work it can vary from time to time, but the point is to work it, no matter what.

I am also experiencing another level of gratitude for program today. Earlier today, my brother came over and was quite upset. He is facing some unsettling circumstances. Thanks to abstinence, working this program, and finding my Higher Power, I found that God enabled me to be present for my brother, to listen to him and focus my attention without lapsing into self-absorption or ego-driven thoughts of self. And by the grace of God, I was able to share with my brother how the Principles embodied in our extraordinary program help me face and deal with life: the people, places, and things that can present daily challenges.

If I was not abstinent today, I could not have been present for my brother because I would have been suffering the anaesthetizing effect of my bingeing food fog or plotting how I was going to cleanse myself of the binge. Either way, when I am in the disease, little room exists for anything or anyone else. Program reinforces that living in active addiction is a full-time job. And thanks to abstinence, OA, God, and members committed to trudging this "Road of Happy Destiny" (*Alcoholics Anonymous*, 4th ed., p. 164) with me, today is another day I am privileged to carry this message of recovery in all of my affairs. The miracle of this simple yet profound program can be a reality for each of us, one day at a time. It does work if we work it.

—September/October 2012

It Doesn't Matter

E very so often, I pass a life milestone and take a moment to wonder where I have been and where I am going.

When I was 10 years old in 1950, I heard that the average life expectancy was only 67 and wondered what my life would be like at the end.

When I was 27, I panicked at the prospect of entering my

30s and leaving my youth behind without having really enjoyed it.

So now having just turned 70, I'm tempted to think about my past and what life may still hold for me. But with OA I've learned the present is the only time that is important.

I bask in the glow of a spring morning. The beauty of spring flowers, a flowering plum, Bradford Pear trees, and the sun's warmth after weeks of cold, stun me. I am thankful for almost four years of abstinence, a 140-pound (64-kg) weight loss, and a strong and healthy body. More important, my heart swells with love, gratitude, and pride for my loving wife, three beautiful and successful adult children, and seven wonderful grandchildren.

But I also revel in your company, "my family of choice" as a fellow OA member described it. You, my OA family, have blessed me with your love, insight, and shares these past few years.

It doesn't matter what tomorrow may bring, how many years I may have, or what I did or didn't do in my past. For today, I am the happiest man in the world.

—*September/October 2012*

12

TOPICS FOR DISCUSSION
AND JOURNALING

The stories of *Taste of Lifeline* can inspire us to reflect on our recovery journey and help us become willing to use the Tool of writing to strengthen our own recovery. Use the questions and prompts in this chapter to journal on your own or as part of writing and discussion time with your sponsor or group.

Chapter One | *Newcomers*

☐ What brought you to OA? Make a list of problems, behaviors, thoughts, and feelings that brought you to OA.

☐ Next to this list make a second list of what you have received. Put an asterisk next to items on the second list that have helped you maintain your recovery the most.

☐ Choose three items from the second list and write about how each item has helped you. Be specific.

Chapter Two | *Steps One to Three*

☐ Honesty is crucial to our ability to take Step One in OA. In what specific ways have you worked a program of "rigorous honesty"?

☐ Are there any ways in which your program has slipped and you've been a little less honest with yourself about your eating?

☐ How have you practiced honesty in other areas of your life?

Chapter Three | *Steps Four to Nine*

☐ Try making a list of your character defects and examining them in relation to the Steps.

☐ Next to each character defect, write one or more Steps you think would help you let go of the defect.

☐ Before you finish, spend time in prayer, meditation, or discussion to cultivate the willingness to let the Steps and your Higher Power direct you toward letting go of your character defects.

Chapter Four | *Steps Ten to Twelve*

☐ Do a "balanced" Tenth Step inventory by making three columns and labeling them "plus," "minus," and "gratitude."

☐ In the plus column, list the things you did well, especially ways you used assets instead of defects and ways you showed love and kindness to others.

☐ In the minus column, list the things you did not do well and any cleaning up you need to do in your life.

☐ In the third column, list all the ways you are grateful, and try to make the third column at least as long as the first two.

☐ Try asking and listening to your HP for guidance with a daily action plan and to determine your role in carrying the message.

Chapter Five | *Tools of Recovery*

☐ How are you applying the OA Tools to your life? Make a row listing the nine Tools: a plan of eating, sponsorship, meetings, telephone, writing, literature, action plan, anonymity, and service.

☐ Under each Tool write three instances where you have applied that Tool successfully in your life.

☐ Separately, list three instances where a life situation went badly.

☐ Then imagine each situation again and how it might have been resolved using the OA Tools.

Chapter Six | *Service and Sponsorship*

☐ Do you believe giving service is an important part of OA and your program of recovery? In OA, what service(s) have you contributed, and how did your actions strengthen your recovery?

☐ As a sponsor, what Tools do you use most to help new sponsees gain a deeper understanding of the Steps and OA program?

☐ How do you help sponsees maintain focus on working all Twelve Steps?

☐ What are some of the rewards of being a sponsor?

☐ As a sponsor, how do you manage your own commitment to abstinence and continue to work the Steps in your daily life?

☐ As a sponsee, what did you look for in your first sponsor relationship?

☐ What do you look for now? Make a list of what your responsibilities are to your sponsor and yourself in the sponsor/sponsee relationship.

☐ How has having a sponsor helped you work the program and find recovery?

Chapter Seven | *Traditions*

☐ What Tradition has helped you the most?

☐ What Tradition is the hardest to apply to your life? (Refer to page 195 for a list of the Twelve Traditions.)

Chapter Eight | *Recovery from Relapse*

☐ If you have experienced relapse, examine why.

☐ Write down the behaviors that prompted it. Next to each reason for your relapse, list some alternative behaviors that might have saved you from that first compulsive bite or eating behavior.

☐ Post your list in a conspicuous place so you know where to find it in an emergency.

Chapter Nine | *Recovery Around the World*

☐ Are you ready to take OA on the road with you during your next great vacation? As you make your travel plans, think about how you will be working the OA program during your trip. Packing a care package is essential and can include things like OA literature, an OA workbook, writing supplies, and a telephone list for outreach calls.

☐ Make a list of the things you will need.

☐ Then make a daily action plan to maintain your recovery journey while you are on your trip.

Chapter Ten | *Long-term Recovery*

☐ This is a threefold disease: physical, emotional, and spiritual, and the three cannot be separated. That means recovery can only be as valuable and powerful as the area in which you have the least recovery. Write down the benefits and challenges of each type of recovery in your program.

☐ Think of new ways of achieving threefold recovery. Make a list.

☐ List all the miracles you see in OA and see if you can add to the list as the miracles grow. Include miracles relating to you at home, with friends, and in the workplace.

☐ Are you surprised by how many miracles fill your life of recovery?

☐ Have you considered lately how OA changed your life? A whirlwind of miracles may have swept away the worst of the past and brought you the best of the present and future. Take stock, write down your observations, and put them in a place where you can grab them when the going gets tough and you need a reminder of how far you've come.

Chapter Eleven | *Gratitude*

☐ How often should you write out a gratitude list? Write a gratitude list and next to each item list who you can thank.

☐ Have you thanked your group lately for all they have given your recovery?

☐ Have you thanked your sponsor? Your Higher Power? Yourself?

1. We admitted we were powerless over food—that our lives had become unmanageable.

2. Came to believe that a Power greater than ourselves could restore us to sanity.

3. Made a decision to turn our will and our lives over to the care of God *as we understood Him.*

4. Made a searching and fearless moral inventory of ourselves.

5. Admitted to God, to ourselves, and to another human being the exact nature of our wrongs.

6. Were entirely ready to have God remove all these defects of character.

7. Humbly asked Him to remove our shortcomings.

8. Made a list of all persons we had harmed and became willing to make amends to them all.

9. Made direct amends to such people wherever possible, except when to do so would injure them or others.

10. Continued to take personal inventory and when we were wrong, promptly admitted it.

11. Sought through prayer and meditation to improve our conscious contact with God *as we understood Him,* praying only for knowledge of His will for us and the power to carry that out.

12. Having had a spiritual awakening as the result of these Steps, we tried to carry this message to compulsive overeaters and to practice these principles in all our affairs.

*Permission to use the Twelve Steps of Alcoholics Anonymous
for adaptation granted by AA World Services, Inc.*

1. Our common welfare should come first; personal recovery depends upon OA unity.

2. For our group purpose there is but one ultimate authority—a loving God as He may express Himself in our group conscience. Our leaders are but trusted servants; they do not govern.

3. The only requirement for OA membership is a desire to stop eating compulsively.

4. Each group should be autonomous except in matters affecting other groups or OA as a whole.

5. Each group has but one primary purpose—to carry its message to the compulsive overeater who still suffers.

6. An OA group ought never endorse, finance, or lend the OA name to any related facility or outside enterprise, lest problems of money, property, and prestige divert us from our primary purpose.

7. Every OA group ought to be fully self-supporting, declining outside contributions.

8. Overeaters Anonymous should remain forever nonprofessional, but our service centers may employ special workers.

9. OA, as such, ought never be organized; but we may create service boards or committees directly responsible to those they serve.

10. Overeaters Anonymous has no opinion on outside issues; hence the OA name ought never be drawn into public controversy.

11. Our public relations policy is based on attraction rather than promotion; we need always maintain personal anonymity at the level of press, radio, films, television, and other public media of communication.

12. Anonymity is the spiritual foundation of all these Traditions, ever reminding us to place principles before personalities.

Permission to use the Twelve Traditions of Alcoholics Anonymous for adaptation granted by AA World Services, In